NEW PULSE 4
Workbook

Michele Crawford
Patricia Reilly

Grammar reference
Writing hub
Advance your vocabulary
External exam trainer
Phrase book
Wordlist

Macmillan Education
4 Crinan Street
London N1 9XW
A division of Macmillan Education Limited

Companies and representatives throughout the world

Level 4 Workbook ISBN 978-1-380-02033-8
Workbook pack ISBN 978-1-380-03976-7

Text © Macmillan Education Limited 2019
Written by Sarah Jackson and Karen Ludlow
Additional material by Jill Leatherbarrow and Anna Cowper

Design and illustration © Macmillan Education Limited 2019

The authors have asserted their right to be identified as the authors of this work in accordance with the Copyright, Designs and Patents Act 1988.

First edition entitled *Pulse* published 2015 by Macmillan Education Ltd
This edition published 2019

All rights reserved. No part of this publication may be reproduced, stored in a retrieval system, or transmitted in any form or by any means, electronic, mechanical, photocopying, recording, or otherwise, without the prior written permission of the publishers.

Original design by Andrew Oliver
This edition design by emc design ltd
Page make-up by SPi Global
Illustrated by: Mark Draisey pp 25, 27, 32, 40, 41, 51, 57,110, 112; Melanie Sharp pp 102, 103, 133; Pablo Velarde pp 18, 27, 33, 51, 58, 59, 106; Tony Forbes pp 4, 8, 19, 34, 43, 59, 72, 105, 107; Matt Ward (Beehive Illustration) pp 102, 136, 137
Cover design by Andrew Magee Design Limited
Cover illustration/photographs by Corbis; Flickr RF; Getty Images/iStockphoto; Getty Images/Radius Images; Westend61.
Picture research by Julie-anne Wilce

The authors and publishers would like to thank the following for permission to reproduce their photographs:

Alamy p105(1), Alamy/Aurora Photos pp20(b),125(tr),129(tr), Alamy/Ines Bazdar p72(l), Alamy/CandyBox Photography p16(cl), Alamy/Catchlight Visual Services p105(7), Alamy/Cultura Creative p110(5), Allamy/Mikael Damkier p56(2), Alamy/DCPhoto p28(tr), Alamy/Phil Degginger p115(tr), Alamy/Design Pics Inc pp105(4),110(8), Alamy/Dinodia Photos p56(5), Alamy/Elena Elisseeva p31(tr), Alamy/Martyn Evans p105(5), Alamy/Malcolm Fairman p116(tr), Alamy/fStop Images GmbH p56(3), Alamy/Hemis p112(t), Alamy/Richard Heyes p107(cr), Alamy/imageBROKER p109(2), Alamy/Image Source pp61(bl),103(5), Alamy/jo ingate p110(2), Alamy/Juice Images p110(3), Alamy/Nathan King p4(5), Alamy/Geof Kirby p119(tr), Alamy/London Entertainment p65(t), Alamy/Oleksiy Maksymenko p31(tr), Alamy/MBI p121(tr), Alamy/keith morris p74(r), Alamy/Nikreates p63(r), Alamy/OJO Images Ltd pp64(bl),110(7), Alamy/Panther Media GmbH p4(6), Alamy/Losevsky Pavel p117(tr), Alamy/PhotoAlto p35(cr), Alamy/photothek images UG/Thomas Koehler p126(tr), Alamy/Pxel p56(1), Alamy/Radius Images pp7(tl),118(tr), Alamy/rumal p110(6), Alamy/Pere Sanz p9(br), Alamy/Solo Stock Events p105(2), Alamy/Sport Picture Library p109(6), Alamy/Andy St John p11(br), Alamy/Travelshots.com/Peter Phipp p73(r), Alamy/Gregg Vignal p15(br), Alamy/A. T. Willett p114(tr), Alamy/Lisa F. Young p105(6); **Daimler AG** p41(br); **Getty Images**/Asia Images Group p36(tc), Getty Images/Thomas Barwick p28(tl), Getty Images/Bettmann p71(tr), Getty Images/Sergei Bobylev p12(t), Getty Images/Jeffrey Coolidge p76(t), Getty Images/Corbis/Push Pictures/Somos p127(tr), Getty Images/Corbis/Tomas Rodriguez p120(tr), Getty Images/Daniel Hurst Photography p75(bl), Getty Images/Design Pics Inc p4(1), Getty Images/Saranga Deva De Alwis p6(cl), Getty Images/Steve Debenport p144(r), Getty Images/Betsie Van der Meer p56(6), Getty Images/digitalskillet p139(cr), Getty Images/Gchutka p19(br), Getty Images/Daniel Grill p4(2), Getty Images/Jamie Grill p34(2)(4), Getty Images/Hero Images p36(cl), Getty Images/kali9 p4(3), Getty images/Sungjin Kim p141(br), Getty Images/Larry Williams & Associates p34(1), Getty Images/Fabrice LEROUGE p34(5), Getty Images/LJM Photo p130(cr), Getty Images/Scott Markewitz p19(tr), Getty Images/martin-dm p130(tr), Getty Images/Walter McBride p50(r), Getty Images/Tara Moore p79(tl), Getty Images/Peter Muller p36(bl), Getty Images/Han Myung-Gu p133(cr), Getty Images/Jordan Naylor p44(r), Getty Images/Oliver Rossi p34(6), Getty Images/Science Picture Co p47(tr), Getty Images/Zave Smith p36(c), Getty Images/Russ Schleipman p20(a), Getty images/Stringer/Han Myung-Gu p132(cr), Getty Images/sturti pp60(tl),111(cr),135(br), Getty Images/Sunny p4(4), Getty Images/Klaus Vedfelt p105(8), Getty Images/wdstock p110(1), Getty Images/Westend61 p32(tr); **Living Lands and Waters** p123(tr); **Macmillan Publishers Ltd** p103(6), Macmillan Publishers Ltd/BANANASTOCK pp27(tl),80(tr), Macmillan Publishers Ltd/ComStock p130(br), Macmillan Publishers Ltd/Corbis/DigitalStock pp7(tr),140(bl), Macmillan Publishers Ltd/Digital Vision p43(cl), Macmillan Publishers Ltd/E+ p75(tr), Macmillan Publishers Ltd/Getty Images pp22(l),38(bl),131(2), Macmillan Publishers Ltd/Getty/iStockphoto pp34(3),145(r), Macmillan Pulbishers Ltd/Getty/iStockphoto/Thinkstock p41(cl), Macmillan Publishers Ltd/Getty/Lightwavemedia/Thinkstock p131(1), Macmillan Publishers Ltd/Image Source pp4(tr),131(3), Macmillan Publishers Ltd/MACMILLAN AUSTRALIA p54(r), Macmillan Publishers Ltd/Moment RF p143(b), Macmillan Publishers Ltd/Photodisc p6(tr); **NASA** p42(cr); **Shutterstock**/Asia Images Group p109(4), Shutterstock/astarot p134(cr), Shutterstock/EPA/Mario Guzman p63(l), Shutterstock/EPA-EFE/PONGMANAT TASIRI p17(br), Shutterstock/Eshma p43(cr), Shutterstock/fizkes p52(tl), Shutterstock/Flotsam p68(r), Shutterstock/Kobal/Warner Bros/Ladd Company p142(br), Shutterstock/Stuart Miles p56(8), Shutterstock/Nejron Photo p39(bl), Shutterstock/Rawpixel.com p26(l), Shutterstock/Oleksii Sidorov p138(br), Shutterstock/sirtravelalot p56(4), Shutterstock/smolaw p56(7); **SWNS Group** p67(t); **Thinkstock**/beardean p103(4), Thinkstock/claudiaveja p109(5), Thinkstock/Comstock Images p66(b), Thinkstock/gbh007 p103(1), Thinkstock/geargodz p109(3), Thinkstock/gemphotography p49(bl), Thinkstock/Ingram Publishing p113(tr), Thinkstock/jenifoto p128(tr), Thinkstock/kissenbo p110(4), Thinkstock/Lumina Stock p10(br), Thinkstock/monkeybusinessimages p124(tr), Thinkstock/Rawpixel p109(1), Thinkstock/John Rowley p105(3), Thinkstock/Titovalrina p103(2), Thinkstock/Wavebreakmedia Ltd p110(4); **WHYY and NewsWorks.org** p122(tr).

Additional Sources:
P36 – Survey data from The American Academy of Child and Adolescent Psychiatry.
P101 - The Theory of Multiple Intelligences, Howard Gardner, 1987, Annals of Dyslexia Vol. 37, Springer.

These materials may contain links for third party websites. We have no control over, and are not responsible for, the contents of such third party websites. Please use care when accessing them.

The inclusion of any specific companies, commercial products, trade names or otherwise, does not constitute or imply its endorsement or recommendation by Springer Nature Limited.

New Pulse conforms to the objectives set by the Common European Framework of Reference and its recommendations for the evaluation of language competence.

Printed and bound in Uruguay

2020
6

CONTENTS

Contents

STARTER	ON HOLIDAY	4
UNIT 1	TEAMWORK	8
UNIT 2	LUCKY ESCAPES	16
UNIT 3	YOUR FUTURE	24
UNIT 4	KEEP IN TOUCH	32
UNIT 5	TECHNOLOGY	40
UNIT 6	YOUR IDENTITY	48
UNIT 7	THAT'S ENTERTAINMENT!	56
UNIT 8	PERSUADING PEOPLE	64
UNIT 9	GET READY FOR YOUR EXAMS!	72

Self-study bank

Grammar reference — Starter unit–Unit 9 — 82–101

Advance your vocabulary — Starter unit–Unit 9 — 102–111

Writing hub — Units 1–9 — 112–129

External exam trainer — 130–147

Phrase book — 148–149

Pronunciation reference — 150

Wordlist — 151–157

Irregular verbs — 158–160

STARTER
ON HOLIDAY

Vocabulary
Describing places

1 Circle the correct words.

I'd love to live in a **pretty** / **dirty** village in the countryside.

1 The centre of the town is very **exciting** / **polluted** because of traffic fumes.
2 It's **safe** / **dangerous** to go swimming in this river because there might be crocodiles!
3 That beach is popular, so it gets **peaceful** / **crowded** at the weekend.
4 That café is very **lively** / **ugly** because lots of students go there.
5 Life in a big city is very **dirty** / **exciting** because there are lots of things to do.

2 Label the pictures with the adjectives in the box.

ancient   comfortable   crowded
expensive   polluted   romantic

1 _____   2 _____
3 _____   4 _____
5 _____   6 _____

Grammar
Present simple and present continuous

1 Complete the text with the present simple or present continuous form of the verbs in brackets.

I (1) _____ (love) this photo! (2) _____ (you / like) it? It (3) _____ (show) me and my friends on holiday in Portugal. We (4) _____ (go) to the same town every year and we (5) _____ (have / always) a great time. In the photo, my friends (6) _____ (try) to carry me along the beach on a surfboard. We (7) _____ (always / enjoy) spending time together, and in this photo we (8) _____ (have) fun. I (9) _____ (remember) that I was in a good mood that day!

2 Write questions about the text in exercise 1.

1 why / she / love / this photo / ?
_____
2 who / it / show / ?
_____
3 what / her friends / do / in it / ?
_____
4 what / they / always enjoy / ?
_____

3 Tick (✓) the correct sentences. Correct the sentences that are wrong.

Lots of British people ~~are visiting~~ Spain every summer. ☐
Lots of British people visit Spain every summer.

1 Lucia's wearing her new swimsuit. ☐
_____

2 It rains at the moment. ☐
_____

3 We aren't usually going abroad for our holidays. ☐
_____

4 My mum never lies in the sun. ☐
_____

5 Do you take a photo now? ☐
_____

6 I'm getting up late every day in the summer holidays. ☐
_____

7 What game are you playing? ☐
_____

Gerunds and infinitives

4 Complete the sentences with the gerund or infinitive form of the verbs in the box.

book   fly   send   take   visit   wait

1 Do you really need _____ everything in that suitcase?
2 I sometimes feel a bit nervous before _____.
3 My friends and I aren't interested in _____ ancient monuments.
4 Nowadays, lots of people use the internet _____ hotels.
5 _____ at airports is really boring!
6 Don't forget _____ me a postcard!

5 Complete the sentences so they are true for you.

When I'm on holiday, …
1 I enjoy _____.
2 I hate _____.
3 I don't want _____.
4 I spend most of my time _____.
5 It's easy _____.

Vocabulary
Holiday activities: verb + noun collocations

1 Complete the verbs. Then, tick the things you did this summer.

Things I want to do next summer!
by Jessica, 16

1 G_____ abroad
2 L_____ on the beach
3 G_____ a suntan
4 S_____ in the sea
5 H_____ a bike
6 V_____ a museum
7 G_____ sightseeing
8 T_____ lots of photos!

2 Complete the replies.

1 I don't want to get sunburnt. → Wear _____!
2 I want to observe life underwater. → Go _____!
3 I'd love to learn about the history of this place. → Visit a _____!
4 I don't want to use public transport to get around the city. → Hire a _____!
5 I want to exercise while I'm on holiday. → Swim _____!

3 Circle the correct words.

1 We're going on a day **journey / trip** to the Space Museum next week.
2 An Australian has become the fastest man to **trip / travel** around the world on foot.
3 The train **journey / voyage** from London to Edinburgh takes about five hours.
4 More than 100,000 people have applied to go on the first **travel / voyage** to Mars.
5 Our camping **journey / trip** was a disaster because it rained every day!

Grammar
Past simple and past continuous

1 Complete the sentences. Use the past simple and the past continuous.

wait for the train / buy some chocolate
While I was waiting for the train, I bought some chocolate.

1. sail in the Mediterranean / see some dolphins
   While we _____.
2. the sun rise / I sleep
   When _____.
3. sit on the beach / have an ice cream
   While they _____.
4. the plane land / the sun shine
   When _____.

2 Complete the dialogue with the past simple or past continuous form of the verbs in brackets.

Simon: (1) _____ (you / have) a nice summer?
Kate: Yes! It (2) _____ (be) the best summer of my life!
Simon: Where (3) _____ (you / go)?
Kate: We (4) _____ (go) to Scotland!
Simon: What (5) _____ (you / do) while you (6) (stay) _____ there?
Kate: Lots of things. One day when we (7) _____ (feel) adventurous, we (8) _____ (climb) a mountain called Ben Nevis! It's the highest mountain in Scotland! On another day we (9) _____ (walk) through a forest when we (10) _____ (see) some beautiful deer! They (11) _____ (stand) together under some trees. It (12) _____ (rain) so they probably wanted to stay dry, just like us.

used to

3 Rewrite the sentences using the correct form of *used to*.

We had a tree house in the garden.
We used to have a tree house in the garden.

1. Amelia didn't like sunbathing.
   _____
2. My friends and I went to the water park every summer.
   _____
3. I loved playing beach tennis.
   _____
4. There weren't any big hotels on the island.
   _____

4 Write questions with the correct form of *used to*.

you / go on holiday with your family / ?
Did you use to go on holiday with your family?

1. you / go to the same place every year / ?
   _____
2. lots of tourists / visit this place / ?
   _____

Comparatives and superlatives

5 Order the words to make sentences.

1. most / the / the / book / This / interesting / in / in / is / library / .
2. isn't / film / as / as / book / good / The / the / .
3. largest / park / city / Which / the / the / is / in / ?

6 Complete the sentences with the correct form of the words in brackets.

1. International travel is getting _____ (cheap)
2. Trains are getting _____ (fast)
3. It's getting _____ (important) to use eco-friendly transport.
4. Train travel is getting _____ (popular)

Listening

1 Listen to Billy giving a presentation to his class about his holiday. Where did he go? 🔊 2

2 Listen again. Correct the sentences.

1 Billy went to a city in the north of France.
   _____
2 The first photo shows Billy sitting in the sun.
   _____
3 The second photo shows an ancient castle.
   _____
4 Billy is in the photo of the city walls.
   _____
5 There is a music festival every August.
   _____
6 The festival events take place in ancient buildings.
   _____

Speaking

3 Complete the following presentation with the phrases in the box. Listen and check. 🔊 3

> As you can see   just the highlights
> In this photo, you can see
> feel free to ask me any questions
> First of all, I'm going to show you
> Today I'm going to talk about

Good afternoon! (1) _____ my summer holiday in Venice, in the north of Italy. I went to stay with my sister who was studying there. (2) _____ some photos of this amazing city. I took a lot so it was difficult to choose only four to include in my presentation! These are (3) _____. After that, (4) _____. Venice is a very beautiful city with lots of pretty squares and lively outdoor cafés. (5) _____ me having lunch at my favourite café next to a canal. (6) _____, I'm eating pizza because it's my favourite food!

Writing

4 Complete the presentation about your summer holiday. Choose three photos to describe.

> Today I'm going to talk about _____.
> First of all, I'm going to show you _____.
> After that, feel free to ask me any questions.
> In this photo, you can see _____.
> In this next photo, you can see _____.
> On another day _____.
> So, I hope you enjoyed looking at some of my holiday snaps. Has anyone got any questions?

📔 LIFELONG LEARNING STRATEGY

Memorizing vocabulary: Spaced repetition

The spaced repetition technique for learning vocabulary is based on the idea that the more often you see a word at increasingly bigger intervals over a period of time, the better you will remember it.

In your notebook, write down six new words from this unit with a translation in your language and an example sentence in English. Test yourself on them again tomorrow and then after 7 days, 20 days and 40 days.

How well did the technique work for you?

1 _____
2 _____
3 _____
4 _____
5 _____
6 _____

More practice

➤ Grammar reference p82
➤ Advance your vocabulary p102
➤ Phrase book pp148–149
➤ Wordlist pp151–157

UNIT 1 TEAMWORK

Vocabulary
Skills and abilities

1 ★ Label the pictures with the words in the box.

> cupcakes   foreign language   juggle
> magic tricks   song   stage   unicycle
> video blog

1 do _____
2 bake _____ 
3 learn to _____ 
4 make a _____ 
5 write a _____ 
6 ride a _____ 
7 perform on _____ 
8 learn a _____ 

LEARNING TO LEARN
Use an online dictionary, such as the Macmillan Dictionary, to help you with your pronunciation. You can use the online dictionary to listen to new words and repeat them after the audio.

2 ★ Match 1–6 with a–f.

1 design   a) first aid
2 play   b) in public
3 edit   c) in a band
4 speak   d) computer code
5 write   e) a website
6 learn   f) photos

3 ★★ Complete the sentences with phrases from exercises 1 and 2.

1 If you _____, you'll know what to do if someone gets hurt.
2 Jade's dad is a chef and he's going to teach us how to _____.
3 It's hard to _____ because it's only got one wheel!
4 I don't want to sing in the school concert because I'm too shy to _____.
5 When you _____, you can change the colours and remove things you don't like.
6 To create your own software, you need to know how to _____.

4 ★★ Complete the sentences so they are true for you.

1 I think _____ is a useful skill.
2 I don't think _____ is a useful skill.
3 I've tried _____, but didn't enjoy it.
4 I'd like to learn how to _____.
5 I think I'd find _____ boring.

5 ★★★ Give reasons for your answers in exercise 4. Write full sentences.

1 _____
2 _____
3 _____
4 _____
5 _____

Grammar

Present perfect with *just, yet, already, for* and *since*

1 Circle the correct words.

1 They haven't gone to bed **already** / **yet**.
2 You're not very late – the class has only **yet** / **just** started!
3 Juan hasn't done his homework **already** / **yet**.
4 I think we've **already** / **yet** met.
5 We're not hungry because we've **just** / **yet** had lunch.
6 I haven't fallen off my unicycle **already** / **yet**!

2 Rewrite the sentences with *just, yet* and *already* in the correct place.

1 They've designed a new class website. It looks great! (just)
_____
2 Can you wait for me? I haven't finished breakfast. (yet)
_____
3 Nick's band has performed live. (already)
_____
4 Wow! She's done a very clever magic trick! (just)
_____
5 Has Sam learned to write computer code? (yet)
_____
6 My friend has spoken in public several times. (already)
_____

3 Complete the sentences with the words in brackets and the present perfect form of the verbs in the box.

> bake   make   not have
> not start   say   see

1 Ella _____ something in Chinese! (just)
2 Our cat _____ (kittens / yet)
3 This is your first week at your new school and you _____ new friends. (already)
4 The match _____ (yet).
5 The kitchen smells nice because we _____ some cupcakes. (just)
6 I think I _____ this film. (already)

4 Write questions with *How long …?* and answers with *for* or *since*.

1 Q _____
(you / have / a pet snake / ?)
A _____
(three years)
2 Q _____
(Tim / play / the drums / ?)
A _____
(he / be / 14)
3 Q _____
(your cousins / live / in Australia / ?)
A _____
(five years)
4 Q _____
(Alice / work / in a circus / ?)
A _____
(February)

5 Complete the dialogue with the correct form of the words in brackets.

Vince: That was great, Dan. How long (1) _____ (you / be) a musician?
Dan: For about six years. I (2) _____ (have) my own guitar since I (3) _____ (be) 12.
Vince: OK, cool. Do you write your own music?
Dan: Yes. Actually, I (4) _____ (just / write) a new song. Do you want to hear it?
Vince: No, that's fine. We (5) _____ (already / hear) you play.
Dan: So would you like me to join the band?
Vince: We (6) _____ (yet / not decide), but we'll call you!

Vocabulary
Life skills

1 ★ Complete the words related to life skills.

1. cr _ _ t _ v _   th _ n k _ n g
2. m _ n _ y   m _ n _ g _ m _ n t
3. c _ _ p _ r _ t _ _ n
4. t _ m _   m _ n _ g _ m _ n t
5. _ c t _ v _   l _ s t _ n _ n g
6. p r _ b l _ m - s _ l v _ n g
7. _ s s _ r t _ v _ n _ s s
8. c _ n f l _ c t   r _ s _ l _ t _ _ n
9. n _ g _ t _ _ t _ _ n
10. _ n t r _ p r _ n _ _ r s h _ p
11. s _ l f - _ w _ r _ n _ s s
12. r _ s p _ c t   f _ r   _ t h _ r s

2 ★ Complete the table.

noun	verb
negotiation	(1) _____
self-(2) _____	be self-aware
money management	(3) _____ money
(4) _____	cooperate
assertiveness	be (5) _____
conflict (6) _____	resolve conflict

3 ★★ Complete the sentences with one word from each box. Which two phrases have a hyphen (-) in the middle?

active   creative   money   problem   self-

awareness   solving   listening
management   thinking

1. My mum knows a lot about _____ _____ because she's a bank manager.
2. Leo enjoys _____ _____ and never gives up until he's found the answer.
3. You have _____ _____ if you know your own strengths and weaknesses.
4. I find _____ _____ difficult because I can never think of new ideas.
5. _____ _____ means paying attention to what the other person is saying.

4 ★★ Read the advert. Match skills 1–5 with phrases a–e.

1) negotiation   __
2) assertiveness   __
3) respect for others   __
4) cooperation   __
5) time management   __

Become a class rep …

and improve school life for all your classmates!

Do you (a) **work well with others** and believe in (b) **treating people with kindness**?

Are you (c) **good at organizing your time**?

Can you (d) **express your opinions with confidence**?

Are you (e) **willing to work to find solutions that everyone is happy with**?

Then apply to be a class rep!

It's a great way to initiate change, develop your skills and it'll look good on your CV.

For more information, contact Mrs Foster.

5 ★★★ Write down a life skill that you have and an example of your actions to illustrate it.

I'm good at time management. I'm never late for school.

Grammar
Present perfect and past simple

1 ⭐ Circle the correct words.

1 We **met** / **'ve met** in front of the cinema at 7.30.
2 Amy **didn't find** / **hasn't found** a job yet.
3 I **took** / **'ve taken** part in a public speaking contest two months ago.
4 He's really happy because he **just heard** / **'s just heard** he won tickets to a concert.
5 Selina **started** / **'s started** making video blogs a year ago.

2 ⭐⭐ Complete the sentences with the words in the box.

ago   for   last   since   when

1 I've learned a lot about money management _____ I opened a bank account.
2 Jake's been secretary of the film club _____ three years.
3 Zoe took her driving test _____ week.
4 They went to a time management workshop six months _____.
5 I met my best friend _____ I was only four years old.

3 ⭐⭐ Complete the second sentence so that it has a similar meaning to the first. Use the words in brackets.

The last time I saw my friends was two weeks ago. (for)
I haven't seen my friends for two weeks.

1 Liz performed on stage for the first time at the age of 16. (was / when)
Liz _____.
2 David bought a bike two years ago. (had / for)
David _____.
3 The last time I swam in the sea I was in Greece last summer. (since)
I _____.
4 Jo's been in America for six weeks. (arrived / ago)
Jo _____.
5 My brother started playing the guitar when he was six. (since)
My brother _____.
6 She became the captain of the hockey team three months ago. (been / for)
Jo _____.

4 ⭐⭐⭐ Complete the paragraph with the present perfect or past simple form of the verbs in brackets.

I (1) _____ (hate) speaking in public since I (2) _____ (be) a child, so when our teacher (3) _____ (ask) us to make a video blog of ourselves for an ICT studies project, I (4) _____ (think) 'Oh no!'. I (5) _____ (not want) to talk in front of a camera, but what could I do? The subject (6) _____ (be) creative thinking and I (7) _____ (enjoy) writing stories and poems for years, so I (8) _____ (decide) to make my video blog about that. I (9) _____ (set up) the video camera on my smartphone a few days ago. Then I just (10) _____ (start) talking about how I get an idea for a story, where I write and so on.

Amazingly, I (11) _____ (not feel) nervous in front of the camera at all! I (12) _____ (not tell) anyone yet, but I feel much more confident as a result of that experience and I might even make another video blog!

Things to do before I'm 17

Being a teenager is the perfect time to try new things you might not do when you're an adult! Last year, when I turned 16, I decided to create my own **bucket list**: ten things to do before I'm 17. Here are the results!

1 *Make a video blog*
I already write a blog, but vlogging was new for me! My vlog is about doing the things on this list. Check it out here. I've really enjoyed learning to vlog and edit videos.

2 *Do more to help people*
I volunteer at a centre for **homeless** people one afternoon a week. I've been a volunteer there for six months now and it's been an amazing experience – it's changed the way I see the world.

3 *Learn to cook*
Well, I'm not an expert cook yet, but I've just made a three-course meal and it wasn't bad!

4 *Learn to ride a moped*
I can ride a moped now, and I've already booked my first driving lesson – for my 17th birthday!

5 *Go on a trip with friends*
We've planned a trip for this summer! I'm going camping near Valencia with some friends for a week. I can't wait!

6 *Do something fun for charity*
I organized a sponsored **shopping trolley** race at school. 50 students took part and we raised over £500 for charity. It was great fun!

7 *Sleep under the stars*
My dad, brother and I **camped wild** in Dartmoor National Park for a weekend – it was fantastic.

8 *Learn survival skills*
Before we went camping, I learnt some basic survival skills. I've also done a first aid course, which could be useful.

9 *Write computer code*
I can't tick this off my list yet, but I did design an app with my friends instead.

10 *Participate in a **flash mob***
I'm definitely still up for the challenge of doing this, but I haven't found one yet. Any suggestions?

My next bucket list will definitely be more ambitious – 18 things to do before I'm 18!

POSTED BY SAM WILSON   Write a comment

Reading

1 Read and listen to the blog post. What is it about? ») 4

a) Sam's goals for next summer.
b) Things Sam has tried to do.

2 Match the words in bold in the blog post with definitions 1–5.

1 a wire basket on wheels, used in a supermarket for shopping _____
2 a large group of people who suddenly gather in a public place and perform and then disappear _____
3 a list of things you want to do before a certain age or during your lifetime _____
4 stayed in a tent, but not in a campsite _____
5 without a place to live _____

3 Read the blog post again. Circle T (true) or F (false).

1 Sam hasn't learned to edit videos yet.   T F
2 Sam started volunteering six months ago.   T F
3 The food that Sam cooked was terrible.   T F
4 Sam can already drive a car.   T F
5 Sam stayed close to Valencia for a week.   T F
6 Sam hasn't written any computer code.   T F

4 Answer the questions. Write full sentences.

1 When did Sam make her list?
_____
2 Where does she do voluntary work?
_____
3 How much money did the school charity event make?
_____
4 Where did Sam and her family go camping?
_____
5 What did Sam design?
_____

Listening

1 Listen to a report about a holiday camp that teaches digital skills. Match people 1–4 with their jobs a–d. 🔊 5

1 Pippa Greendale   a) camp instructor
2 Jane Brookes   b) participant
3 Daniel Baker   c) reporter
4 Chloe Garcia   d) camp director

2 Listen again and complete the information about the camp.

Teen Tech Camp

Location: (1) _____ Hampton
Duration of camp: (2) _____
When: (3) in _____, half-term holiday
Age of participants: 12 to (4) _____
Activities: building (5) _____, making video blogs, designing (6) _____, creating computer games
Skills taught: Writing (7) _____, using different kinds of software
Projects uploaded to: Teen Tech Camp (8) _____

3 Answer the questions. Write full sentences.

1 What are Teen Tech Camp participants allowed to keep when the camp finishes?
 _____
 _____

2 What does Daniel Baker do during the rest of the year?
 _____
 _____

3 What three aspects of their computer game have the people in Chloe's group invented?
 _____
 _____

4 What does Chloe often do in her free time?
 _____
 _____

5 What will people be able to access on the Teen Tech Camp website?
 _____
 _____

Speaking

4 Complete the dialogue with the phrases in the box. Listen and check. 🔊 6

> for example   good at   interested in
> often say that   some experience of
> what I find most exciting about

Amelia: Why do you think you'd be suitable for a summer job at Rollercoaster World?
Laurie: Well, I'm (1) _____ communicating with others and people (2) _____ I'm very polite too.
Amelia: And can you stay calm in difficult situations?
Laurie: Yes, definitely. (3) _____, if a customer was rude to me, I wouldn't get angry.
Amelia: OK, great. We're looking for someone who can also work as part of a team.
Laurie: That's not a problem for me. I've got (4) _____ cooperating with others because I've been a member of a volleyball team for two years.
Amelia: And what appeals most to you about working at Rollercoaster World?
Laurie: (5) _____ this opportunity is that it would give me experience of working in the leisure industry. I'm (6) _____ a career in this area in the future.
Amelia: I see. Well, thanks very much for coming in today, Laurie. We'll be in touch by the end of the week.
Laurie: Thanks. It was a pleasure to meet you.

Writing

5 Circle the correct words.

1 My sister is **a bit** / **pretty** good at public speaking.
2 Amber is **a bit** / **not very** good at managing her time.
3 Chinese is a **really** / **quite** hard language to learn.
4 I'm not **very** / **quite** shy so I don't want to perform on stage.
5 Our new neighbours are **not very** / **a bit** strange. They don't always say 'hello'.

Progress check

Vocabulary
Skills and abilities

1 Circle the correct words.

1 Try to make me look good when you **write / edit** those photos!
2 How do you **play / do** magic tricks like that?
3 Rachel had to learn **first aid / to juggle** when she was training to be a nurse.
4 My dad paid someone to **design / write** a website for his company.
5 Joe has a lot of experience of speaking in **a band / public**.
6 You need a good sense of balance to ride **a unicycle / computer code**.
7 Helen's **made / performed** a video blog and posted it on YouTube.

Life skills

2 Read the definitions and complete the words.

1 The ability to express your opinions confidently. a_____
2 Using your imagination to come up with ideas. c_____ t_____
3 The ability to organize your time. t_____ m_____
4 You find answers to difficult questions. p_____-s_____
5 You have this when you know what kind of person you are. s_____-a_____
6 This takes more effort than hearing. a_____ l_____
7 You treat people with kindness. r_____ f_____ o_____
8 This describes the situation where people work well together. c_____
9 This results in a peaceful solution to a disagreement. c_____ r_____
10 This is what you need in order to start your own business. e_____
11 This is often necessary when people with different points of view try to agree about something. n_____
12 You're good at this if you use your money sensibly. m_____ m_____

Grammar
Present perfect with *just, yet, already, for* and *since*

3 Write sentences using the present perfect and the words in brackets.

1 come back later; / I / not finish / ! (yet)
   _____
2 we / hear / the good news (just)
   _____
3 they / left / the party (already)
   _____
4 my best friend / not tell / me / her secret (yet)
   _____
5 we / be / best friends / we were / babies (since)
   _____

Present perfect and past simple

4 Complete the sentences with the present perfect or past simple form of the verbs in the box.

be   get   give   lose   not see   start

1 Katie _____ the results of her violin exam yesterday.
2 I _____ Paul for days. I think he's on holiday.
3 Oh no! Mum _____ her mobile phone again!
4 We _____ in Berlin since Tuesday, but we're leaving tomorrow.
5 Savita _____ her blog last year.
6 My sister _____ me this cookbook for my birthday two years ago.

5 Correct the sentences.

1 How long you've had a class website?
   _____
2 I'm hungry because I didn't have lunch yet.
   _____
3 Cheryl's performed on stage last Friday.
   _____
4 I've finished already this exercise.
   _____
5 My dad's played the piano for he was 12.
   _____
6 I've taken the cupcakes out of the oven two minutes ago.
   _____

Extension

UNIT 1

Cumulative vocabulary

1 Match the sentence beginnings with the endings.

1 The magician created the illusion ___
2 She worked as a volunteer ___
3 We're going to do a workshop ___
4 You should list all your skills and qualifications ___
5 It's important to update your website regularly ___
6 We need someone to keep the minutes ___

a) about how to become entrepreneurs.
b) on your CV.
c) for a children's charity.
d) of walking on water.
e) at the next committee meeting.
f) with any new information.

2 Complete the sentences with the correct form of the words in brackets.

1 Annie is _____ of her personal strengths and weaknesses. (awareness)
2 He needs to learn how to _____ his money better. (manager)
3 I wish I was better at having ideas and thinking _____. (creative)
4 She's shy, so it's difficult for her to _____ herself in big groups. (assertive)
5 If we try, I'm sure we can find a _____ to this problem. (solve)
6 You must learn to _____ and help each other more! (cooperation)
7 One of the more difficult life skills to learn is conflict _____. (resolve)
8 Every time I ask my parents for something it becomes a big long _____. (negotiate)

More practice

- Grammar reference p84
- Advance your vocabulary p103
- Writing hub p112
- Phrase book pp148–149
- Wordlist pp151–157

Cumulative grammar

3 Circle the correct words.

Project Trust

(1) **Do you think / Are you thinking** about taking a year out before you go to university or start a job? If the answer is 'yes', Project Trust can help! We (2) **arrange / 're arranging** voluntary work placements in Asia, Africa, Latin America and the Caribbean for 17–19 year-olds.

Read what these volunteers (3) **said / were saying** about their experiences.

I went (4) **living / to live** in Namibia in Africa for a year with Project Trust. While I (5) **was working / worked** on a local newspaper there, I (6) **'ve made / made** many new friends and the experience (7) **was providing / provided** me with many different skills. I used to (8) **being / be** very shy but since I came home, I (9) **'ve become / became** much more confident and assertive. I would recommend it to anyone!

Carla, Spain

I've (10) **just / already** come back from India, where I (11) **'ve taught / was teaching** English in a primary school. Standing in front of a class for the first time was pretty scary, but I (12) **survived / have survived** and even started (13) **enjoy / to enjoy** it! I (14) **use / used** to be a bit irresponsible, but I (15) **really grew / 've really grown** up as a result of my experiences with Project Trust.

Nick, UK

15

UNIT 2 LUCKY ESCAPES

Vocabulary
Rescue and survival

1 ⭐ **Circle the correct words.**

1. The only **compensation** / **survivor** of the helicopter accident is recovering in hospital.
2. Wearing a seatbelt can protect you if your car **crashes** / **capsizes**.
3. Search and rescue **victims** / **workers** have found five people alive after a building collapsed on them.
4. If wood is dry, it can catch **fire** / **firefighters** very easily.
5. **International** / **First** aid has been sent to Chile after a major earthquake.
6. A team of **casualties** / **paramedics** treated passengers at the scene of the train crash.

2 ⭐⭐ **Match words 1–6 with definitions a–f.**

1. victims   ___
2. capsize   ___
3. give first aid   ___
4. casualties   ___
5. firefighters   ___
6. compensation   ___

a) boats do this if they turn over in the water
b) you do this to someone who is injured
c) they often rescue people from burning buildings
d) people who are affected by a disaster
e) money you can receive if you're in an accident that wasn't your fault
f) people who are injured or killed in a war or an accident

3 ⭐⭐ **Complete the sentences with the correct form of the words in the box.**

| capsize   give first aid   international aid |
| paramedics   receive compensation |
| survivors |

1. She isn't breathing! Does anyone know how to _____?
2. The victims' families deserve to _____ for the suffering they've been through.
3. A plane has crashed in the Indian Ocean and, tragically, there are no _____.
4. _____ has been sent, but food and medical supplies aren't reaching the people who need them.
5. When my boat _____, I kept telling myself that I was going to be rescued.
6. I will always be grateful to the highly skilled team of _____; without them I wouldn't be alive today!

4 ⭐⭐⭐ **What would you do in these situations? Complete the sentences.**

1. You're at school and there's an earthquake.
   I'd _____.
2. You're cooking and a pan catches fire.
   I'd _____.
3. You're walking in the mountains with a friend when she falls and injures her leg.
   I'd _____.
4. You're walking on the beach when you see a boat capsize.
   I'd _____.
5. What sort of international aid do you think it would be useful to send survivors of a natural disaster?
   I think it would be useful to send _____
   _____.

16

Grammar
Past perfect and past simple

1 ⭐ **Complete the sentences with the past perfect form of the verbs in brackets.**

1. Sabina _____ (not experience) an earthquake before she lived in Japan.
2. We _____ (put out) the fire by the time the firefighters arrived.
3. Mum was worried about me because I _____ (forget) to call her.
4. The driver admitted that he _____ (not stop) at the traffic lights.
5. They _____ (give up) hope of finding any survivors, but then they heard a shout.

2 ⭐⭐ **Order the words to make sentences. Add a comma (,) where necessary.**

1. hospital / been / fell off / hadn't / my bike / I / before / to / I / .
2. seen / late / the car / the train driver / By the time / was / had / it / too / .
3. made / called / Joanna / the boy / comfortable / an ambulance / after / had / she / .
4. dark / the helicopter / had / it / gone / arrived / By the time / .
5. Doctors / his heart / after / brought / stopped / back to life / had / him / .
6. she / checked / before / jumped / Jasmine / out of the plane / had / her parachute / .

3 ⭐⭐ **Complete the sentences with the past simple or past perfect form of the verbs in brackets.**

1. A father and son _____ (survive) by swimming to the nearest island after their boat _____ (capsize) in a storm.
2. He _____ (tell) the police what he _____ (see) and took them to the scene of the accident.
3. After I _____ (help) the man get out of his car, I _____ (call) the emergency services.
4. I _____ (realize) that I _____ (forget) to turn off the gas and I rushed home.
5. Jenny _____ (already leave) the building when it _____ (catch) fire.
6. The rescuers _____ (find) a man who _____ (break) his leg during the hurricane.

4 ⭐⭐⭐ **Complete the text with the past simple or past perfect form of the verbs in the box.**

| call | flood | rescue | stop |
| survive | take | travel | try |

A football coach in Thailand (1) _____ his team on a trip to explore some caves. They (2) _____ a long way inside the caves when it started to rain. The boys (3) _____ to return to the entrance of the caves but they couldn't because some of the caves (4) _____. Instead, they had to go deep inside the caves to escape the rising water. After the boys' parents (5) _____ the emergency services for help, it took nine days to find the boys. A team of rescue workers and paramedics successfully (6) _____ all 12 boys and their coach. The boys (7) _____ by drinking water from the cave walls and they (8) _____ never _____ hoping that they would find a way out.

Vocabulary
Extreme adjectives

1 ⭐ Label the pictures with the adjectives in the box.

> boiling   disgusting   exhausted
> freezing   furious   huge   starving   tiny

1  _____   2 _____

3  _____   4 _____

5  _____   6 _____

7 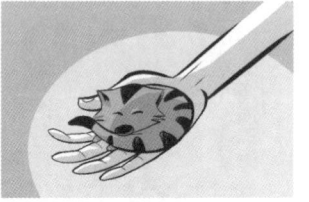 _____   8 _____

2 ⭐ Circle the correct words.

1 The girl suffered **horrific** / **terrifying** injuries, but she made a full recovery.
2 My friends sent me some **gorgeous** / **unforgettable** flowers when I was in hospital.
3 I was **fascinating** / **delighted** when I heard the good news!
4 This documentary about mountain climbing is **gorgeous** / **fascinating**.
5 When the roof of the house blew off, it was **terrifying** / **unforgettable**.
6 Working as a voluntary firefighter was a(n) **gorgeous** / **unforgettable** experience.

3 ⭐⭐ Complete the sentences with extreme adjectives. In some cases, there is more than one possible answer.

1 When you're the pilot of a plane, one _____ mistake can cause a disaster.
2 Lucy Irvine wrote a _____ book about living on a tropical island for a year.
3 The most _____ meal I've ever eaten was raw octopus!
4 Trying to survive alone in the desert must have been a/an _____ experience.
5 Joe Simpson's book about a disastrous climbing trip was a _____ success and made him famous.

📔 LIFELONG LEARNING STRATEGY

Describing things and experiences

When you're describing things and experiences, avoid repeating common adjectives like *good* and *bad*. Use extreme adjectives to make your descriptions more interesting.

Rewrite the sentences. Replace the underlined words with extreme adjectives.

1 It was very stormy and the waves were <u>very big</u>!
_____
2 The programme about UFOs was <u>very interesting</u>.
_____
3 The air conditioning wasn't working and it was <u>very hot</u>.
_____
4 The view from our tent was <u>very nice</u>.
_____

4 ⭐⭐⭐ Answer the questions. Write full sentences.

1 What is the most fascinating place you've ever visited?
_____
2 What is the most disgusting food you've ever eaten?
_____
3 What makes you furious?
_____
4 What is the most terrifying experience you've ever had?
_____

Grammar
Subject and object questions

1 ⭐ Are these subject or object questions? Write S (subject) or O (object).

1. Who rescued the girl? __
2. What did you do at the weekend? __
3. Who lives in that house? __
4. What did Paul take on the camping trip? __
5. Who is going hiking? __

2 ⭐⭐ Write questions with *Who ...?*

Someone taught Sam to make a fire.
<u>Who taught Sam to make a fire?</u>

1. The dog rescued a man.
   _____
2. Someone rang the police.
   _____
3. The search and rescue workers found someone.
   _____
4. Someone had a skiing accident yesterday.
   _____
5. The ambulance took someone to hospital.
   _____

3 ⭐⭐ Write questions using the past simple.

1. what / make / you / fall off / your bike / ?
   _____
2. who / cause / the accident / ?
   _____
3. what / the car driver / say / to you / ?
   _____
4. who / take / you / to hospital / ?
   _____
5. what / time / the accident / happen / ?
   _____

4 ⭐⭐⭐ Read the text. Then write the questions about Andrea for these answers.

Andrea Kristensen

I love the mountains and I learned to ski when I was six. Once, there was a terrible avalanche and my friend nearly died. The mountain rescue team saved her life and that's when I decided that I wanted to become a mountain rescuer. I did a first aid course at the age of 16 and I got my Mountain Rescue Qualification when I was 18!

What <u>does Andrea love</u> ?
The mountains.
1. What _____?
   To ski.
2. Who _____?
   Her friend.
3. Who _____?
   The mountain rescue team.
4. What _____?
   That she wanted to become a mountain rescuer.
5. What _____?
   Her Mountain Rescue Qualification.

5 ⭐⭐⭐ Imagine you are interviewing the lifeguard in the picture about his job. Write five questions with *What ...?* or *Who ...?*

1. _____
2. _____
3. _____
4. _____
5. _____

A

A dog was **reunited** with its owners four months after they thought she had drowned. The Griffith family were sailing on their yacht close to the Great Barrier Reef in Australia when there was an enormous storm. The family survived uninjured, but their pet, Sophie, a three-year-old dog, fell **overboard**. The Griffith family had given up all hope of finding Sophie alive when they heard about a dog that matched her description living on a remote island near where she had disappeared.

Sophie had swum over ten kilometres through the shark-infested ocean to the island of St Bees, where she had survived by hunting small animals. Park rangers on the island were surprised to discover that the dog, which they had believed to be wild, was a family pet! Sophie is now recovering from her **ordeal** at home in Queensland.

B

A teenager who tried to find a **short cut** through the woods when he was skiing, got lost near Sugarloaf Mountain in the Maine area last weekend. 17-year-old Nicholas Joy had arranged to meet his father in the car park, but when he didn't **show up**, his father realized something was wrong.

Search and rescue teams spent two days and nights looking for the teenager, who had no food with him when he went missing, but extreme weather conditions made their task very difficult.

When a volunteer firefighter found the boy, he was tired, cold and **starving**. He had survived two nights in freezing cold temperatures by making a shelter out of snow and tree branches, using a technique he'd learned from a reality show on television. He'd also tried to make a fire by rubbing two sticks together – another skill which had been taught on the programme – but hadn't succeeded.

Reading

1 Read and listen to two news stories. Choose the headlines which match them.

A
- Abandoned Dog Swims Home
- Happy Ending For Shipwrecked Dog

B
- Injured Skier Has Lucky Escape
- TV Programme Saves Boy's Life

2 Match the words in bold in the texts with definitions 1–6.

1. unpleasant experience   _____
2. route that is quicker than the usual way   _____
3. brought together again   _____
4. very hungry   _____
5. off a boat   _____
6. appear   _____

3 Read the news stories again. Circle T (true), F (false) or DS (doesn't say).

1. A dog and its owners nearly drowned. T F DS
2. The dog lived in the wild for several months. T F DS
3. The dog's owners didn't recognize her when they saw her again. T F DS
4. Nicholas Joy is an experienced skier. T F DS
5. He used two different methods to stay alive. T F DS
6. He learnt survival skills on a special course he did. T F DS

4 Answer the questions. Write full sentences.

1. How did Sophie become separated from her owners?
2. Why was her journey to St Bees dangerous?
3. Why did Nicholas Joy lose his way?
4. What made it hard to look for him?
5. What hadn't Nicholas managed to do?

Listening

1 Listen to a talk about the adventurer Erik Weihenmayer and match names 1–4 with what they describe a–d. ◁)) 8

1. *Blindsight*
2. *The Seven Summits*
3. *Expedition Impossible*
4. *No Barriers USA*

a) an organization
b) some mountains
c) a film
d) a TV programme

2 Listen again. Choose the correct answers.

1. What happened when Erik Weihenmayer was a teenager?
   a) He had an accident.
   b) He went blind.
   c) Someone made a film about him.
2. How did Erik Weihenmayer make history?
   a) By climbing one very famous mountain.
   b) By climbing several mountains.
   c) By doing several different extreme sports.
3. Which of the following activities didn't Erik have to do on *Expedition Impossible*?
   a) cycling
   b) kayaking
   c) climbing
4. Who does *No Barriers USA* help?
   a) Anyone who has experience of war.
   b) Anyone who was born with a disability.
   c) Anyone who wants to overcome his / her physical problems.
5. What is the film about?
   a) A group of students who climbed Mount Everest on their own.
   b) A group of students who climbed part of Mount Everest.
   c) Some blind adults who learned how to climb.

3 Answer the questions. Write full sentences.

1. Which mountains did Erik climb before his Everest expedition?
   _____
2. How many people were there in Erik's *Expedition Impossible* team?
   _____
3. How long did it take to prepare the Tibetan group for the climb up Mount Everest?
   _____
4. What was amazing about their achievement?
   _____

Speaking

4 Complete the conversation with question tags. Listen and check. ◁)) 9

Ana: This rucksack is too heavy!
Lucy: Well, you'll have to take some things out, (1) _____?
Ana: I suppose so. But what?
Lucy: Think about it. We're going camping on a beach, (2) _____?
Ana: Yes.
Lucy: Well, we won't have any electricity, (3) _____?
Ana: Er, no.
Lucy: You don't need a hairdryer, then, (4) _____?
Ana: OK, I'll take it out!
Lucy: What's in this bottle?
Ana: Insect repellent! That's really important, (5) _____?
Lucy: Yes, that's true! We got lots of mosquito bites last time we went camping, (6) _____?

Writing

5 Order the sentences to make a news report.

The girl who fell out of the sky

☐ a) Then she saw a small stream and decided to follow it, hoping that it might lead to a village or town.

[1] b) Juliane Koepcke was only 17 years old when the plane she was flying on was struck by lightning during a terrible storm over the Amazon.

☐ c) Finally, after she had walked for nine days, she met some local people who rescued her and took her to hospital.

☐ d) It took Juliane a whole day to get out of her seat and climb down to the ground.

☐ e) Its engines had failed and Juliane was the only survivor after the plane fell three kilometres out of the sky.

☐ f) At first, when she reached the ground, she couldn't stand up, but eventually she managed to start moving.

Progress check

Vocabulary
Rescue and survival

1 Complete the words.

1 Survivors of the plane crash have received c_____ of thousands of pounds.
2 A team of p_____ attended to the injured people.
3 The boat c_____ because there were too many people on board.
4 Always keep a f_____ a_____ kit in your car in case someone has an accident.
5 The number of c_____ from the disaster has reached 58.
6 5,000 people are now homeless, v_____ of the earthquake.
7 We desperately need i_____ a_____ because food and medical supplies are running out.
8 F_____ say that they now have the forest fires under control.

Extreme adjectives

2 Circle the correct words.

1 Trying to survive alone in the jungle must have been a **furious** / **horrific** experience!
2 I was absolutely **starving** / **freezing**, but the only food in my rucksack was some chocolate.
3 There was a **gorgeous** / **delighted** view from the top of the mountain.
4 The Grand Canyon is so **huge** / **tiny** that many people get lost there every year.
5 After walking for eight hours, we were absolutely **exhausted** / **disgusting**!
6 Take lots of water and a hat with you because in the summer it is **fascinating** / **boiling**!

Grammar
Past perfect and past simple

3 Circle the correct words.

1 My arm **hurt** / **had hurt** because I **broke** / **'d broken** it!
2 Fiona **was** / **had been** worried because she **heard** / **'d heard** about the accident on the news.
3 By the time the police **arrived** / **had arrived**, someone **called** / **had called** an ambulance.
4 When **did you realize** / **had you realized** that lightning **struck** / **had struck**?
5 I **didn't see** / **hadn't seen** a forest fire before I **lived** / **'d lived** in Australia.

4 Complete the text using the past perfect or past simple form of the verbs in brackets.

27-year-old Lyndi Harding took a deep breath and jumped out of the plane. She (1) _____ (do) several parachute jumps before and nothing (2) _____ (go) wrong. This time, however, on a skydiving trip to California with friends, her parachute (3) _____ (fail) to open and she (4) _____ (fall) a kilometre through the air before hitting the ground. When she woke up in hospital, doctors told her that she (5) _____ (break) her nose and two ribs among other injuries, but she would be OK. They thought she (6) _____ (lose) consciousness before she (7) _____ (hit) the ground, making her body more relaxed, and this (8) _____ (save) her life.

Subject and object questions

5 Write subject or object questions using Who …? or What …? for the information in bold.

1 The firefighter rescued **the cat**.
_____
2 **The firefighter** rescued the cat.
_____
3 The boy made a shelter from **snow**.
_____
4 **The neighbours** called the police.
_____

Extension

Cumulative vocabulary

1 Complete the sentences with the words in the box.

> damage   equipment   flooding
> injuries   lightning

1. You need good ropes and other special _____ to go climbing in the mountains.
2. There's a man in America who has been struck by _____ six times!
3. The hurricane caused a lot of _____ to buildings and many trees were blown down.
4. Many parts of the country experienced _____ after the heavy rains.
5. The climber had been lost for two days, but didn't have any serious _____.

2 Complete the text with the words in the box.

> base camp   collapse   crevasses
> expeditions   stuck   summit

Climbing Everest

Climbing Mount Everest is always dangerous, even for experienced climbers, because of the extreme weather conditions. (1) _____ can only take place at certain times of the year, usually between April and May. Climbers must first reach the (2) _____, which is already 5,600 metres high. This is as far as you can go before you need to start using special equipment, but you are still 20 kilometres from the (3) _____ of the mountain. Next, you climb through the Khumbu icefield which is especially dangerous because the ice is always moving and sometimes parts of the ice (4) _____. You can also easily fall into one of the many deep (5) _____ and get (6) _____. The last part of the climb is very difficult but the view when you finally reach the top and the feeling you get are unparalleled.

More practice

- Grammar reference p86
- Advance your vocabulary p104
- Writing hub p114
- Phrase book pp148–149
- Wordlist pp151–157

Cumulative grammar

3 Choose the correct answers.

Alice: I (1) _____ a brilliant film last night. It was called *Captain Phillips*. (2) _____ it?
Sam: No, but my dad (3) _____ it a couple of months ago.
Alice: What (4) _____ of it?
Sam: He really liked it, but we (5) _____ the same kind of films! What (6) _____ about, anyway?
Alice: It's the true story of some pirates who hijack a ship and how the captain tries to save the lives of his crew.
Sam: Who (7) _____ the part of the captain?
Alice: Tom Hanks. I (8) _____ like him, but he's really good in this film.
Sam: What about the other actors?
Alice: They're all excellent! I (9) _____ of the film before I (10) _____ it, but I was really impressed.
Sam: I really want (11) _____ it now! Can you send me the link?
Alice: Yes, I've (12) _____ sent it to you!

1. a) 've watched   b) watched   c) was watching
2. a) You've seen   b) Saw you   c) Have you seen
3. a) saw   b) seen   c) 's seen
4. a) he thought   b) did he think   c) 's he thinking
5. a) don't usually like   b) don't like usually   c) aren't usually liking
6. a) does it   b) it's   c) 's it
7. a) plays   b) 's playing   c) does play
8. a) used not   b) didn't use to   c) wasn't used to
9. a) didn't hear   b) haven't heard   c) hadn't heard
10. a) downloaded   b) was downloading   c) 'd downloaded
11. a) seeing   b) to see   c) see
12. a) yet   b) already   c) since

UNIT 3 YOUR FUTURE

Vocabulary
Future aspirations

1 ★ Match the verbs with the words.

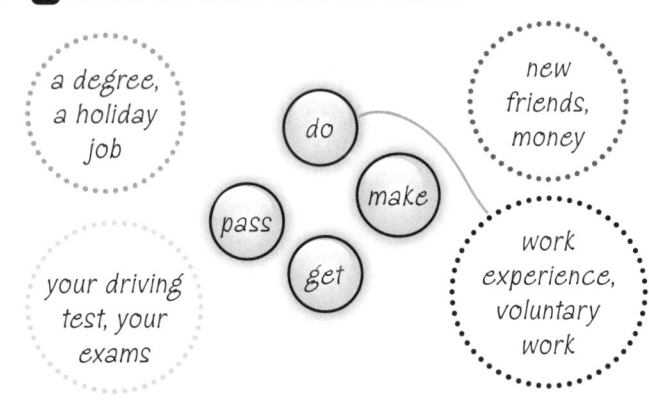

- do
- make
- pass
- get

- a degree, a holiday job
- new friends, money
- work experience, voluntary work
- your driving test, your exams

LIFELONG LEARNING STRATEGY

Collocations

In English, many verbs with a similar meaning collocate (or go together) with particular nouns. For example, we say 'speak a language' but 'tell a story'. Make lists of these phrases in your vocabulary notebook (e.g. *speak* + noun) and every time you hear a new collocation, add it to the list.

2 ★ Complete the phrases with *do* or *make*.

1 _____ the housework
2 _____ a decision
3 _____ a choice
4 _____ your homework
5 _____ arrangements

3 ★★★ Complete the sentences with the phrases in the box.

> apply for a job   go backpacking
> go for an interview   go on an exchange
> leave home   study abroad

1 George likes living with his parents and he doesn't want to _____.
2 Lily is going to _____ with a school in Hamburg.
3 Sam always wanted to _____ in South-East Asia and do some volunteering along the way.

4 In order to _____, you have to be fluent in a foreign language.
5 You should always include your CV when you _____.
6 You should dress smartly when you _____.

4 ★★★ Match phrases 1–6 with comments a–f.

1 get a degree ___
2 go on an exchange ___
3 do voluntary work ___
4 go backpacking ___
5 go for an interview ___
6 do work experience ___

a They asked me a lot of questions and I was really nervous.

b While I'm at college, I'm working on a local newspaper one day a week to learn more about journalism.

c This certificate is the result of four years of studying!

d My friend and I have a small budget to travel round France this year. It will be fun travelling on buses and trains to get around.

e I'm going to stay with a student from a school in Britain. Later he'll come to stay with me in Spain.

f I really enjoy helping others and I'm not bothered about making money.

5 ★★★ What do you want to do before you are 25? Write six things below in the order you want to do them.

1 I want to _____.
2 _____
3 _____
4 _____
5 _____
6 _____

Grammar
Future tenses

1 ⭐ **Complete the sentences with *will*, *won't* or *might*.**

1 Lucy _____ leave home. She wants to work abroad. (✓)
2 Michael _____ study art at university. It's his dream. (✓)
3 Sue _____ pass her driving test next week. (?)
4 Simon _____ buy a car. He can't afford it. (✗)
5 Amy _____ need help finishing the housework. (?)
6 I _____ help her. (✓)

2 ⭐⭐ **Write questions about Ian using the present continuous. Then write short answers.**

visit a centre for homeless people (hospital)
Is Ian visiting a centre for homeless people?
No, *he's visiting a hospital.*

1 do voluntary work with adults (children)
_____
No, _____.
2 take them on a trip (play games with them)
_____
No, _____.
3 spend the whole day there (the morning)
_____
No, _____.
4 talk to any doctors
_____
Yes, _____.

3 ⭐⭐ **Write what Christine intends to do before her job interview. Use *be going to*.**

1 think of some questions to ask about the job
_____
2 borrow some smart clothes from her mum
_____
3 not take the car
_____
4 check the train times
_____
5 not go to bed late the night before
_____

4 ⭐⭐ **Circle the correct words.**

1 We've got to go because we **'re meeting** / **'ll meet** Jo for a coffee.
2 This job sounds fun. I think I **'ll apply** / **'m applying**.
3 Hurry up! The bus **leaves** / **is leaving** at nine o'clock!
4 I need a favour. **Are you going to help** / **Will you help** me write a CV?
5 Lena **isn't going** / **doesn't go** on the exchange trip to Italy.
6 As a lifeguard, you **won't earn** / **aren't earning** as much as a lawyer.
7 I **give** / **'m giving** a presentation to 100 people tomorrow and I'm a bit nervous!
8 Who **'ll** / **'s** going to pay for your driving lessons?

5 ⭐⭐⭐ **Complete the dialogue with the correct future form of the verbs in brackets.**

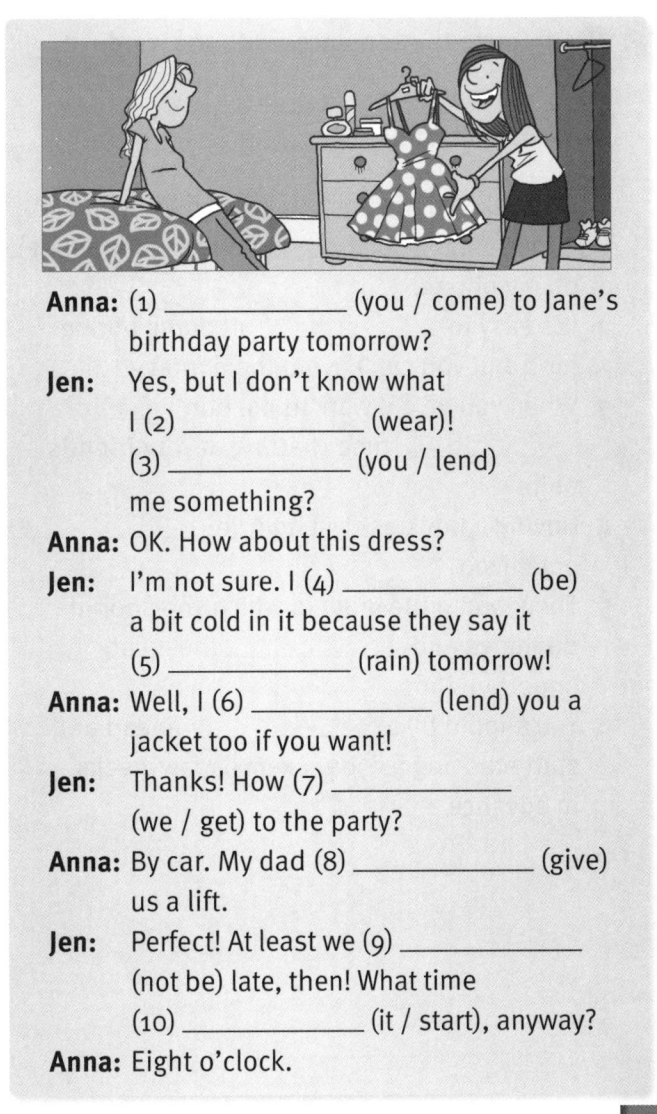

Anna: (1) _____ (you / come) to Jane's birthday party tomorrow?
Jen: Yes, but I don't know what I (2) _____ (wear)!
(3) _____ (you / lend) me something?
Anna: OK. How about this dress?
Jen: I'm not sure. I (4) _____ (be) a bit cold in it because they say it (5) _____ (rain) tomorrow!
Anna: Well, I (6) _____ (lend) you a jacket too if you want!
Jen: Thanks! How (7) _____ (we / get) to the party?
Anna: By car. My dad (8) _____ (give) us a lift.
Jen: Perfect! At least we (9) _____ (not be) late, then! What time (10) _____ (it / start), anyway?
Anna: Eight o'clock.

Vocabulary
Time management

1 ⭐ **Match 1–6 with a–f.**

1 make   a) a break
2 meet   b) a goal
3 take   c) a deadline
4 find   d) a routine
5 set   e) a list
6 develop   f) a balance

2 ⭐ **Complete the sentences with the words in the box.**

> get   plan   prioritize   put   set   waste

1 If I think I might forget to do something important, I _____ a reminder about it on my phone.
2 It's easy to _____ off doing boring jobs, but you can't avoid them forever!
3 When you've got work to do, don't _____ time chatting to your friends online.
4 Having a tidy desk will help you _____ organized.
5 Think about the order in which you should do things and _____ the most important jobs.
6 You should try to _____ ahead and start studying for your exams a few weeks in advance.

3 ⭐⭐ **Match the phrases in the box with the definitions.**

> develop a routine   meet a deadline
> plan ahead   put something off
> set goals   take a break

1 finish a piece of work on time _____
2 have a rest _____
3 give yourself tasks to complete _____
4 think about the things you need to do in the future _____
5 do the same things at the same times every day _____
6 decide to do something that you don't want to do another day _____

4 ⭐⭐ **Match problems 1–6 with advice a–f.**

1 I'm really tired! ___
2 I spend all my time studying and haven't got any hobbies! ___
3 I waste a lot of time sending messages to my friends when I should be working. ___
4 I often forget what I've got to do. ___
5 I find it difficult to meet deadlines. ___
6 I never have enough time to do everything I want to do. ___

a) Switch off your phone when you're doing your homework.
b) Plan ahead and don't leave everything till the last minute.
c) You'd better take a break.
d) Prioritize the tasks that are the most important.
e) You need to find a balance between work and free time.
f) Make a list of your tasks for each day.

5 ⭐⭐⭐ **Think of four ways to improve your time management skills. Write full sentences.**

1 I could _____.
2 _____
3 _____
4 _____

Grammar
Future continuous

1 ⭐ Complete the sentences with the future continuous form of the verbs in brackets.

1 At four o'clock I _____ (do) my homework.
2 At five o'clock I _____ (chat) to my friends.
3 At six o'clock I _____ (have) a driving lesson.
4 At ten o'clock I _____ (watch) a film in the living room.
5 At eleven o'clock I _____ (lie) in bed, reading a novel.
6 At midnight I _____ (sleep).

2 ⭐ Complete the sentences about the girl in exercise 1. Use the future continuous form of the verbs in brackets.

1 At four o'clock she _____ (not play) football.
2 At six o'clock she _____ (not make) a sandwich.
3 At seven o'clock she _____ (not study).
4 At ten o'clock she _____ (not feed) her dog.
5 At eleven o'clock she _____ (not have) a shower.
6 At midnight she _____ (not listen) to music.

3 ⭐⭐ Complete the sentences with the future continuous form of the verbs in the box.

feel   go   leave   say   take

This time next year I …
1 _____ home!
2 _____ to university.
3 _____ goodbye to all my friends.
4 _____ all my things with me.
5 _____ nervous, but excited!

4 ⭐⭐ Write questions using the future continuous.

what / you / do / this time tomorrow / ?
_____
1 who / you / sit / next to at lunch tomorrow / ?
_____
2 what job / you / do / in ten years' time / ?
_____
3 how much / money / you / make / ?
_____
4 you / live / in the UK / ?
_____
5 you / feel / happy / ?
_____

5 ⭐⭐⭐ Answer the questions in exercise 4. Write full sentences.

1 _____
2 _____
3 _____
4 _____
5 _____
6 _____

SO YOU WANT TO BE A PROFESSIONAL?

So you're talented but are you **dedicated** enough to your hobby or sport to become a professional? We spoke to two teens who are working hard to turn their **passion** into a future career.

WINSTON GEORGE

This September I'll be starting at the Royal Ballet School in London. They only take 20 new students every year and I'm going to be one of them. I still can't believe it!

I'm different from other students because I only started ballet at 14, two years ago. Before that I was a hip-hop dancer. It was my PE teacher who made me try ballet – I didn't want to go to my first lesson! But I loved it and now my goal is to become a professional dancer. At the school I'll be dancing for at least four hours every day and I know it will be difficult at first, but I'm determined to do well.

The biggest challenge for me will be the *pas de deux* – dancing with a partner – because I haven't had much practice. You sometimes lift your partner over your head and you have to be strong. I've got the strength but I'm not very tall for my age. I hope I'll grow another five centimetres at least by the time I'm 18!

FEMI WILSON

I live in London, but my dad is Brazilian and I started Capoeira when I was eight. I love it, in fact I'm a bit **obsessed** by it! I sometimes practise for 4–5 hours a day. I want to be a champion and start my own Capoeira school one day, but at the moment my mum wants me to prioritize studying for my GCSEs! I know she's right and I need to get some **qualifications** but I'm competing in the European championships in September so I need to train.

Next year I'll be 16 and I hope I'll be studying in São Paulo with a famous *Mestre* (Capoeira master), but I don't know if he's accepted me yet. I'm small and slim, like my mum, and sometimes people are surprised that I have such a good **level**. The Mestre said I needed to improve my singing – yes you need to sing in Capoeira, too – so I'm going to work very hard on that over the summer.

Reading

1 Read and listen to the text. Complete the profiles.))) 10

Name	Winston George	Femi Wilson
Age		
Sport / Hobby		
Plans for September		
Future plans		

2 Read the text again. Write *Winston* or *Femi*. Who:
1 has practised their sport / hobby since they were very young? _____
2 wasn't excited about starting their sport / hobby? _____
3 is aware that it will be challenging to begin with? _____
4 would like to be taller? _____
5 surprises people because he / she is very good? _____

3 Match the words in bold in the text with the definitions 1–5.
1 thinking about something all the time _____
2 how good you are at something _____
3 when you give time and energy to something _____
4 a strong feeling of love or hate _____
5 what you get for passing exams _____

4 Correct the sentences so they are true.
1 Winston always wanted to try ballet dancing.
_____
2 He hopes he'll get stronger in the future.
_____
3 Femi's parents are Brazilian.
_____
4 She disagrees with her mum who says she should study more.
_____

Listening

1 Listen to an advert for a TV programme and complete the information. 🔊 11

Title of programme: _____
Prize: _____
Age of competitors: 16 to _____

2 Listen again. Match candidates 1–5 with five of the characteristics a–g.

1. Kaya ___
2. Felix ___
3. Bibsi ___
4. Ben ___
5. Linda ___

a) honest
b) determined
c) shy
d) demanding
e) hardworking
f) competitive
g) modest

3 Answer the questions.

1. What FOUR types of challenge do the teams have to face? Complete the information
   a) complete a _____
   b) solve a _____
   c) give an original _____
   d) _____ a great _____
2. Who will help the teams complete their tasks?
   _____
3. Which members of the team know the most about technology?
   _____
4. Who are the sporty and who are the musical members of the team? Which instruments do they play?
   _____
5. What are Kaya and Bibsi both good at?
   _____
6. Which tasks are the team going to do on Friday?
   _____

Speaking

4 Complete the interview with the expressions in the box. Listen and check. 🔊 12

> I look forward to hearing from you
> It's been a pleasure   Please take a seat
> Pleased to meet you
> thanks for coming in today
> We'll let you know our decision

Beth: Hello, Neil. I'm Beth Jacobs and I'm the director of Help the Homeless.
Neil: Hello. (1) _____.
Beth: (2) _____.
Neil: Thanks!
Beth: So why are you interested in doing voluntary work with us?
Neil: Well, I'd like to help the local community in some way and I really admire the work you do with homeless people.
Beth: I see. And have you got any particular skills that you could offer?
Neil: Well, I'm quite a good cook. My parents have got a restaurant so I've got experience of cooking for lots of people.
Beth: That's great. So you'd be happy working in the kitchen, then?
Neil: Yes, very.
Beth: Excellent. Well, (3) _____, Neil.
Neil: Thanks. (4) _____ to meet you.
Beth: (5) _____ in a couple of days.
Neil: Great. (6) _____.

Writing

5 Complete the CV with the headings in the box.

> Education and training
> Personal information   Personal skills
> Position applied for   Work experience

1 _____

Becky Howard
12 Fores Road, Doncaster, DN35 OAB
becky.howard@blacklines.com

2 _____
Temporary post as summer camp tutor

3 _____
Sept 2019–June 2020: Taking GCSEs in Mathematics, English language, Science, French, History, Geography

4 _____
Jan 2018–Present: Editor of online school magazine
July–Aug 2018: Volunteer, St Helen's Hospital Library

5 _____
Mother tongue: English
Other language(s):   French

Progress check

Vocabulary
Future aspirations

1 Circle the correct words.

1 My aunt **got** / **studied** her degree from Harvard University.
2 Most companies want you to send your CV when you apply for a(n) **interview** / **job**.
3 When I went **backpacking** / **on an exchange** to Germany, I had to go to school every day!
4 Did you **do** / **make** lots of new friends at summer camp?
5 Paul passed his **driving test** / **exams** the third time he took it.
6 You aren't old enough to leave **abroad** / **home** and live on your own!
7 If you get a **voluntary** / **holiday** job, you'll earn money and have fun.

Time management

2 Complete the sentences with the phrases in the box.

> find a balance   get organized
> make lists   meet a deadline
> plan ahead   put off   set goals
> take a break   waste time

1 Let's _____ and get some fresh air!
2 It's important in any job to _____ between work and free time.
3 I _____ of words in English and stick them on my bedroom wall.
4 Anna decided to _____ telling her parents the bad news.
5 Don't _____ playing games when you should be working!
6 If you can't _____ for a piece of work, explain to your teacher why you need more time.
7 _____ for the new school year by buying a notebook to write your homework in.
8 When arranging a trip, it's a good idea to _____ and book tickets early.
9 To achieve your dreams, _____ and do something towards achieving those dreams every day.

Grammar
Future tenses

3 Choose the correct answers.

1 What are you planning to do when you finish school?
   a) I'm going to go on a trip round the world.
   b) I'll go on a trip round the world.
2 Do you want to come and study at my house tonight?
   a) No, I can't. I'll take our cat to the vet.
   b) No, I can't. I'm taking our cat to the vet.
3 When can I expect to hear from you?
   a) We'll call you in a few days' time.
   b) We're calling you in a few days' time.
4 Will we have to get up early tomorrow?
   a) Yes! Lessons are going to start at nine o'clock.
   b) Yes! Lessons start at nine o'clock.
5 Why are you taking your umbrella with you?
   a) Because it'll rain!
   b) Because it might rain!
6 Why is Rick wearing trainers to the interview?
   a) He's changing when he gets there.
   b) He's going to change when he gets there.
7 What time does the train leave?
   a) I don't know.
   b) I'm not knowing.
8 Will you study at Granada University?
   a) No, I won't get good enough grades.
   b) No, I don't get good enough grades.

Future continuous

4 Complete the dialogue with the future continuous form of the verbs in brackets.

Dom: Are you busy on Sunday?
Rosa: Yes. I (1) _____ (help) my dad in our café all day.
Dom: What (2) _____ (you / do)?
Rosa: I (3) _____ (serve) food, but I (4) _____ (not cook)!
Dom: Looks like I (5) _____ (watch) that new film by myself then!

Extension

Cumulative vocabulary

1 Complete the dialogue with the words in the box.

> accommodation   exchange   excursions
> host family   location   sightseeing

A: So what are your plans this summer, Ali? Are you doing anything interesting?
B: I'm going on a(n) (1) _____ trip to Washington DC. I've never been before and I'm really excited about it!
A: That's exciting and Washington is a great (2) _____ for your first trip to the States. There'll be lots of things to see and do. What kind of (3) _____ are you staying in?
B: With an American (4) _____ the Andersons. They've got a daughter, Rose, who is the same age as me and she'll be coming to stay with us in the autumn.
A: That will be really good for your English, won't it? So do you know what activities you'll be doing?
B: There are lots of (5) _____. What I'm most looking forward to is going to New York. We're only going for one day though, so I hope there will be enough time for all the (6) _____ I want to do.

2 Match the sentence beginnings with the endings.

1. We got up very early and **set off** ___
2. My dad likes to **start off** the day ___
3. The teacher has **put off** the exam ___
4. Unfortunately, our aeroplane can't **take off** yet ___
5. At the end of the day, I like to **switch off** ___

a) because so many people are ill.
b) and relax by listening to music.
c) on our journey as soon as the sun rose.
d) with several cups of strong coffee.
e) because there are some technical problems.

More practice
- Grammar reference p88
- Advance your vocabulary p105
- Writing hub p116
- Phrase book pp148–149
- Wordlist pp151–157

Cumulative grammar

3 Complete the message with the correct form of the verbs in brackets.

Hi Erica,

Sorry I (1) _____ (not be) in touch recently, but I (2) _____ (just / start) a holiday job at the Aqualand Water Park! We used (3) _____ (come) here a lot when we were younger – (4) _____ (you / remember)?
I (5) _____ (enjoy) the job, but it's a bit tiring because I (6) _____ (work) from 9am till 3pm nearly every day. Here's a photo of me at work. What (7) _____ (you / think)?!

Something amazing (8) _____ (happen) last week! I (9) _____ (sell) tickets for one of the rides when I (10) _____ (see) Jason! He (11) _____ (come) for a day out with his brother. Anyway, he said he might (12) _____ (call) me this weekend and I was really happy. Then I remembered – I (13) _____ (work) all weekend ☹!
I (14) _____ (let) you know what happens …
What are you planning to do this summer? (15) _____ (you / get) a job?
Bye for now,

Justine

PS I miss you! (16) _____ (you / come) and see me at the Aqualand Water Park one day?

UNIT 4
KEEP IN TOUCH

Vocabulary
Phrasal verbs

1 ⭐ Match sentences 1–5 with pictures a–e.

1 Emily and Fran have **fallen out**. ___
2 Joe's dad **told** him **off**. ___
3 Daisy's **looking after** her little brother. ___
4 Nick's **going out** with Ana! ___
5 Sophie **gets on** well with her mum. ___

2 ⭐⭐ Replace the words in bold with the correct form of the phrasal verbs in the box.

> ask out   bring up   hang out   make up
> meet up   settle down   split up

1 American parents **raise** their children differently from Japanese parents.
_____
2 In Europe, people often get married and **live a quieter life** when they're in their 30s.
_____
3 My mum and dad **separated** when I was four years old. _____
4 I think Finn is going to **invite me to go on a date with him**! _____
5 Let's **get together** and go bowling this weekend! _____
6 My brother and I had a big argument yesterday, but we've **forgiven each other** now.
_____
7 Sue often **spends time** with her friends at the beach. _____

3 ⭐⭐⭐ Complete the text with the phrasal verbs in the box.

> bring up   fall out   get on
> hang out   look after   tell off

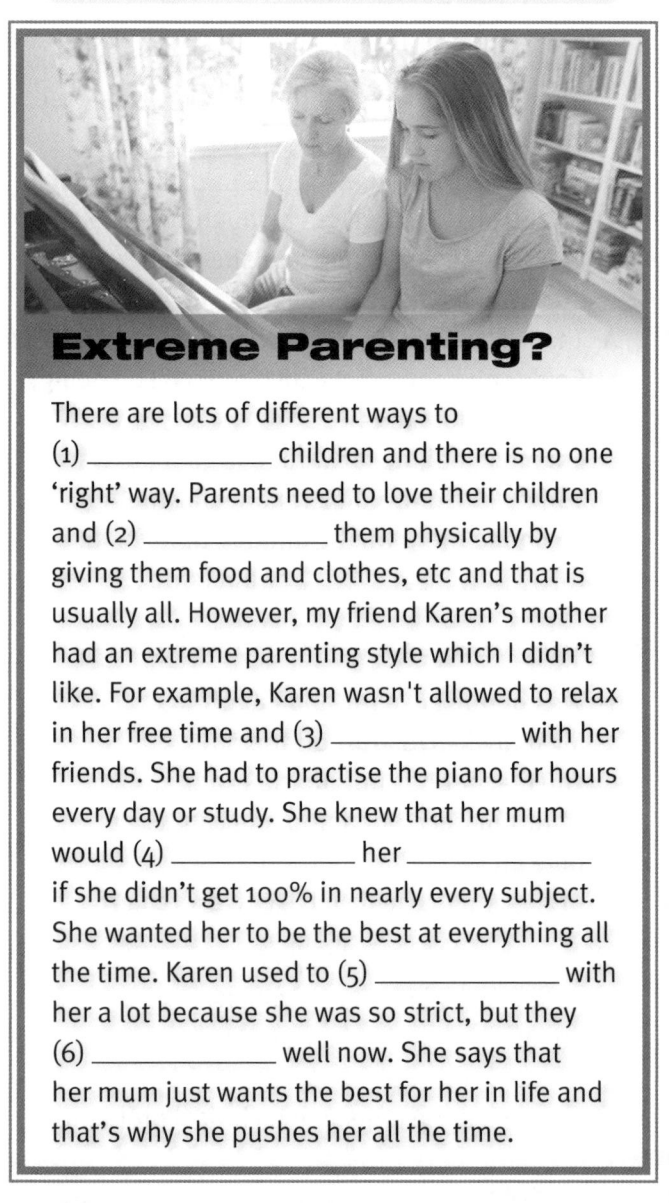

Extreme Parenting?

There are lots of different ways to (1) _____ children and there is no one 'right' way. Parents need to love their children and (2) _____ them physically by giving them food and clothes, etc and that is usually all. However, my friend Karen's mother had an extreme parenting style which I didn't like. For example, Karen wasn't allowed to relax in her free time and (3) _____ with her friends. She had to practise the piano for hours every day or study. She knew that her mum would (4) _____ her _____ if she didn't get 100% in nearly every subject. She wanted her to be the best at everything all the time. Karen used to (5) _____ with her a lot because she was so strict, but they (6) _____ well now. She says that her mum just wants the best for her in life and that's why she pushes her all the time.

4 ⭐⭐⭐ Write five sentences about how your parents brought you up.

1 _____
2 _____
3 _____
4 _____
5 _____

Grammar
The zero, first, second and third conditional

1 ★ Order the words to make first conditional sentences.

1 you / rude to him / if / 're / Your dad / shout / will / .
   _____

2 Mum / worried / be / late / I / Will / if / 'm / ?
   _____

3 forgive / I / apologizes / she / Amber / won't / unless / .
   _____

4 complain / Lauren's parents / will / help / the housework / doesn't / if / with / she / .
   _____

5 my mobile phone / 'll / with / take / go out / me / if / I / .
   _____

2 ★★ Complete the second conditional sentences. Use *would* or *wouldn't* to make them true for you.

1 My parents _____ (be) angry if I _____ (have) a tattoo.
2 If I _____ (take) a funny photo of a friend, I _____ (put) it on Facebook.
3 If I _____ (lose) ten euros, I _____ (tell) my parents.
4 I _____ (fall out) with a friend if he or she _____ (tell) me a lie.
5 I _____ (feel) hurt if my friends _____ (forget) my birthday.

3 ★★★ Complete the third conditional sentences with the correct form of the verbs in brackets.

1 If I _____ (not like) Dan, I _____ (not write) that text message.
2 If I _____ (click) on the right name, Dan _____ (got) the message.
3 If the message _____ (go) to Dan, David _____ (not receive) it.
4 If David _____ (not get) the message, we _____ (not go out) together.
5 If we _____ (not go out) together, I _____ (not know) that he was so nice!

4 ★★★ Complete the conditional sentences in the dialogue with the correct form of the verbs in brackets.

Mum: Would you mind if I (1) _____ (stop) you using your mobile phone and computer for a week?
Holly: Yes!!! How (2) _____ (I / keep) in touch with my friends if you did that?
Mum: Well, there are lots of ways. You could call them on the landline, for example.
Holly: But if they (3) _____ (put) photos on Facebook, I wouldn't see them!
Mum: Yes, but it would only be for a week. If you agree, it (4) _____ (be) an experiment.
Holly: What for?
Mum: To see what life is like without electronic communications. If you (5) _____ (be) born 20 years ago, you wouldn't have had a mobile phone and a computer, you know!
Holly: Well, if I take part in this experiment, (6) _____ (you / do) me a favour?
Mum: OK, I will, unless you (7) _____ (ask) me for something completely unreasonable.
Holly: It's a deal!

Vocabulary
Non-verbal communication

1 Label the pictures with the words in the box.

> frown   gesticulate   hold hands
> shake hands   smile   stare

1 _____
2 _____
3 _____
4 _____
5 _____
6 _____

2 Match 1–6 with a–f.

1 make
2 give somebody
3 shrug
4 raise
5 kiss somebody
6 roll

a) your shoulders
b) your eyebrows
c) on the cheek
d) your eyes
e) a hug
f) eye contact

3 Choose the correct answers.

What do people sometimes do when they're …

1 pleased to see somebody they know well?
   a) frown
   b) give him/her a hug
2 surprised?
   a) make eye contact
   b) raise their eyebrows
3 annoyed with somebody?
   a) roll their eyes
   b) kiss him/her on the cheek
4 in love?
   a) shake hands
   b) hold hands
5 not sure about something?
   a) stare
   b) shrug their shoulders

4 Complete the sentences with words from exercises 1 and 2. Make any necessary changes.

1 I was embarrassed when my grandma _____ me on the cheek in front of my friends!
2 Hugh is very shy and doesn't make eye _____ when he talks to you.
3 My sister was crying, so I gave her a _____ to make her feel better.
4 What are you looking at? Don't you know that it's rude to _____?
5 When I asked Sebastian what was wrong, he just shrugged his _____.

5 When was the last time you did these things? Write full sentences.

1 smiled
_____
2 frowned
_____
3 gave somebody a hug
_____
4 shook hands with somebody
_____
5 kissed somebody on the cheek
_____

Grammar
Adverbs of possibility and probability

1 ⭐ **Match adverbs 1–4 with their meanings a–c. Two adverbs have the same meaning.**

1 maybe
2 definitely
3 perhaps
4 probably

a) It's certain.
b) It's likely.
c) It's possible.

2 ⭐ **Circle the correct words. In one sentence both are possible.**

1 This is **definitely / perhaps** Megan's phone because that's a photo of her family on it!
2 **Maybe / Perhaps** Aaron didn't say 'hello' because he didn't see you.
3 I **probably / definitely** won't go out tonight, but I'm not sure yet.
4 **Perhaps / Probably** I'll call you later; I won't be going to bed early tonight.
5 **Definitely / Maybe** Chloe likes me because she sat next to me on the bus this morning.

3 ⭐⭐ **The adverbs in these sentences are in the wrong place. Rewrite the sentences correctly.**

1 You shouldn't tell your parents that joke definitely.
   _____
2 Sean probably is still in bed because he came home at 3am!
   _____
3 You'd like to tell the rest of the class maybe what you're talking about!
   _____
4 We should make perhaps friends with Sabina because she seems nice.
   _____
5 I won't definitely tell anybody your secret.
   _____

4 ⭐⭐⭐ **Rewrite the sentences using the adverbs in brackets.**

I'm not sure Mike got my message yesterday. (maybe)
Maybe Mike didn't get my message yesterday.

1 I know my mum will find out if I lie to her. (definitely)
   _____
2 I don't think I'll call Gemma tonight. (probably)
   _____
3 Tom might be angry because you criticized his friend. (perhaps)
   _____
4 Are you sure that you can trust Nicole? (definitely)
   _____
5 It's possible that somebody took my phone by mistake. (maybe)
   _____

5 ⭐⭐⭐ **Answer the questions using adverbs of possibility and probability. Write complete sentences.**

What would you do if …
1 a friend said something to hurt your feelings?
   _____
2 you met somebody at a party and wanted to see him or her again?
   _____
3 your best friend didn't like your boyfriend/girlfriend?
   _____
4 your parents read the messages on your phone?
   _____
5 a friend asked you to lie about something to his/her parents?
   _____
6 you saw a friend copying in an exam?
   _____

Social media and mental health

Some doctors have suggested that social media might not be good for teens' mental health, but a recent study reports that 75% of teens in the USA have at least one social media account, and 51% say they log onto social media sites at least once every day. Should parents be worried? We don't know enough about the long-term effects of social media use, so we decided to ask some teenagers about their own experiences.

Lee: I've noticed that spending time on social media can make me feel **anxious**. For example, if I see photos of my friends at a party I didn't go to, I start worrying about whose party it was and why I wasn't invited. My sister told me that there's a name for this feeling – FOMO – fear of **missing out**! Sometimes social media just feels like a competition. It's easy to start believing that everyone else is having a better time than you and feel **depressed** about your own life. I hate that.

Hanna: Personally, I **rely on** social media to make me feel better when I'm depressed! My friends and I send each other jokes and silly videos if one of us is having a bad day. But I try to stay away from photo-sharing sites. I don't like them because there is a **pressure** to look perfect. I know some girls who spend ALL their free time trying to take the best selfies with perfect hair and make-up and all that. It's easy to start believing that these things are really important, but they aren't.

Jack: I like being able to stay in contact with my friends. But there's a bad side to this too: you can never get away! People expect you to answer texts immediately and I feel like I always need to know what people are doing. I check my phone all the time and I'm always worried I'm missing something. My parents say that I've forgotten how to **concentrate** properly and I think they could be right.

Laila: I use blogging sites to meet people from different countries and practise my English. And, before you ask, yes my parents DO know about it and they don't mind as long as I tell them what I'm doing. I also follow YouTubers who post videos about making soap and shampoos from natural products. I've become good friends with some of them and I hope to start my own soap business one day. I think social media is great if you know how to use it.

Reading

1 Read and listen to the article. Which person ... 🔊 13
1. likes social media for some things but doesn't like photo-sharing? _____
2. thinks that social media mostly makes them feel stressed and worried? _____
3. believes social media is a good thing if you use it in the right way? _____
4. believes that social media might be affecting their ability to pay attention? _____

2 Match the words in bold in the text with definitions 1–6.
1. to direct your attention completely towards something _____
2. worried and nervous _____
3. feeling of being forced to do something you might not want to do _____
4. not to get the chance to do or enjoy something good _____
5. very unhappy and without hope _____
6. to trust something and expect it will always do certain things _____

3 Read the article again. Choose the correct answers.
1. Social media makes Lee feel worried that ...
   a) he doesn't have enough friends.
   b) a social activity is happening that he isn't included in.
   c) he doesn't go to enough parties.
2. Hanna thinks that photo-sharing sites
   a) are only for people who like taking lots of selfies.
   b) make people think the wrong things are important.
   c) put people under pressure to share private photos.
3. Jack is worried that checking his phone all the time
   a) makes his parents angry.
   b) is bad for his concentration.
   c) isn't the best way to stay in contact with his friends.
4. Laila
   a) says her parents don't like her going online.
   b) thinks social media is a bad thing if you don't use it every day.
   c) mainly uses YouTube and blogging sites.

Listening

1 Listen to three conversations. Match them with the means of communication in the box. 🔊 14

> face-to-face interaction
> mobile phone call   video chat

Conversation 1 _____
Conversation 2 _____
Conversation 3 _____

2 Listen again and write J (Jess), M (her mum), A (Adam) or G (her grandma).

Who …
1 is invited to a birthday celebration? __
2 has sent something that hasn't arrived? __
3 makes a different suggestion? __
4 has a habit of being late? __
5 is video chatting for the first time? __
6 disagrees with somebody about something? __, __

3 Answer the questions. Write full sentences.

1 How does Jess usually celebrate her birthday?
_____

2 How many people does she want to invite to the meal?
_____

3 What doesn't Adam eat?
_____

4 Why does Jess tell her grandma off?
_____

Speaking

4 Complete the discussion between a teacher (T), Natalie (N), Lydia (L) and Mark (M) with the words in the box. Listen and check. 🔊 15

> ask   for   opinion   personally   think

T: If a friend of yours started getting nasty messages from somebody, what advice would you give him or her?
N: (1) _____, I think the best thing to do in a situation like that is to ignore the messages, so that's what I'd tell my friend.
L: I agree. I (2) _____ that if cyberbullies don't get a reaction, they usually give up.
M: I disagree. If you (3) _____ me, it would be better to tell your friend to go to somebody like a teacher. They could then put a stop to the bullying before it got more serious.
L: (4) _____ me, that would be the last resort. I'd suggest discussing it with his or her parents first.
M: No, in my (5) _____, a teacher would have a better idea of what to do.
T: Well, thank you all for contributing to this discussion.

Writing

📓 LIFELONG LEARNING STRATEGY

Formal and informal language

When doing a writing task, it's important to use the right language for the task. If you're writing a letter of application for a job, you should use formal language, but if you're writing a message to a friend, you should use informal language.

Match the formal expressions with the informal expressions with a similar meaning.

1 good
2 I'm surprised.
3 I agree.
4 That's a pity.
5 a little
6 I look forward to hearing from you.

a) Me too.
b) Speak soon!
c) Oh no!
d) a bit
e) cool
f) No way!

5 For 1–4, order the words to make sentences.

> Hi Harriet,
> (1) going / 's / it / How / ?
> _____
>
> I can't come shopping tomorrow morning. ☹ I've got a piano lesson.
> (2) annoying / It / so / 's / !
> _____

> What time does your lesson finish?
>
> 12.45
>
> Well, let's go shopping afterwards.
>
> Great idea! (3) Mum / give / town / a / into / lift / us / can
> _____
>
> Cool. (5) now / for / Bye / !

Progress check

Vocabulary
Phrasal verbs

1 Complete the text with the words in the box.

after   down   off   on   out (x3)   up

My best friend, Gemma, and I get (1) _____ really well. Even when one of us is going (2) _____ with somebody or has a lot of school work, we always find time to hang (3) _____ together. I feel I can always be honest with her and she feels the same way. She tells me (4) _____ when I'm being too bossy, for example! Sometimes we fall (5) _____ about silly things, but we always make (6) _____ again! Maybe it's because neither of us has got any brothers or sisters that we always look (7) _____ each other. One day, I suppose we'll both get married, settle (8) _____ and have our own children, but I know we'll be friends forever.

Non-verbal communication

2 Circle the correct words.

1. On the last day of school, our teacher **shook** / **held** hands with us all.
2. The man didn't speak English so he communicated by **rolling his eyes** / **gesticulating**.
3. When I saw Toby **smiling** / **frowning**, I knew he was angry about something.
4. Babies can **make eye contact with** / **give hugs to** people from the moment they're born.
5. My dad **shrugged** / **raised** his eyebrows in surprise when he saw my new hairstyle.
6. In some parts of France, people **kiss** / **stare** each other on the cheek four times when they meet.

Grammar
The zero, first, second and third conditional

3 Write first conditional questions.

1. When / you / be / older / have / children / ?
   _____
2. you / let them / wear / whatever / they / want / ?
   _____
3. If they / not study at school / how react?
   _____

4 Complete the second conditional sentences in the text with the correct form of the verbs in the box.

fall out   feel   leave   not be (x2)   not know

My best friend, Kim, is really important to me. If I (1) _____ her, my life (2) _____ the same. We tell each other everything. If we (3) _____, I (4) _____ really upset, but we never argue. I get on really well with my parents too. They want me to go to university but, if I (5) _____ school and got a job, they (6) _____ angry. They think I should make my own decisions.

5 Rewrite the sentences in the third conditional.

1. They missed the bus so they were late.
   _____
2. I didn't know it was your birthday so I didn't buy you a present.
   _____
3. Alex got bad marks because he hadn't studied.
   _____

Adverbs of possibility and probability

6 Complete the sentences with *maybe*, *perhaps*, *probably* or *definitely*. In some cases, there is more than one possible answer.

1. Sam's _____ coming to the party. He said he's almost certain he can make it.
2. _____ I'll go to the party. I'm not sure.
3. If Ellen doesn't call you, _____ you could call her.
4. I _____ think people look more attractive when they smile.

38

Extension

UNIT 4

Cumulative vocabulary

1 Complete the text with the words in the box.

> active body language communication
> distracted eye contact facial expressions
> frowning interrupt multi-task nodding

Suzie Jones is a relationship coach. She helps her clients improve their (1) _____ skills and get on better with the important people in their lives. '(2) _____ listening is one of the best things you can do to improve your relationships,' she says. 'You have to learn to make (3) _____ with the other person and use the right (4) _____ to show that you are giving them your full attention. (5) _____ are also very important – very simple things such as smiling rather than (6) _____ and (7) _____ your head, not shaking it – make a big difference.' She thinks that all the phones and digital devices we have these days don't help our relationships because people get (8) _____ too easily. 'Don't try to (9) _____ when someone is talking to you', she says, 'listen and only listen, and, most importantly of all, let the other person finish what they are saying, don't (10) _____.'

More practice

- Grammar reference p90
- Advance your vocabulary p106
- Writing hub p118
- Phrase book pp148–149
- Wordlist pp151–157

Cumulative grammar

2 Circle the correct words.

Tim: You (1) **don't / not** look very happy. What's the matter?

Sue: Liz and Amanda (2) **had / have** just had an argument and now they (3) **don't talk / aren't talking** to each other.

Tim: Not again!

Sue: Yes! Sometimes I think life would be easier if I (4) **didn't / wouldn't** have any friends!

Tim: (5) **Maybe you / You maybe** should do what the Japanese do and rent some new ones!

Sue: What (6) **mean you / do you mean**?

Tim: Well, I (7) **'d read / was reading** a magazine at the dentist's yesterday and I (8) **found / 've found** a really interesting article about 'rent-a-friend' agencies in Japan.

Sue: What are they?

Tim: I (9) **didn't hear / hadn't heard** of them before, but basically they allow you to hire people to be your friends!

Sue: No way! Why would anybody do that?

Tim: Well, for example, if you wanted to have a party, but you didn't know many people, you (10) **might / 'll** want to invite some fake friends (11) **to make / making** it a bit livelier!

Sue: But how does that work? If they (12) **weren't / aren't** real friends, won't it be obvious to other people?

Tim: Not necessarily. The article says that the people who work for these agencies (13) **always play / play always** their roles very well!

Sue: Well, it's an interesting idea, but I don't really see the point of it. I'd rather just be honest with other people.

Tim: So you (14) **won't / wouldn't** be interested if somebody opened a 'rent-a-friend' agency here?

Sue: No, but Liz and Amanda might!

UNIT 5 TECHNOLOGY

Vocabulary
Innovation and invention

1 ⭐ **Label the pictures.**

1 _____ smartphone   2 e-_____

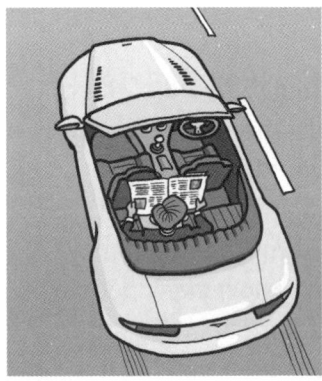

3 _____ car   4 space _____

2 ⭐ **Match 1–8 with a–h. Which answer is written as one word?**

1 high-speed   a) gadgets
2 bio   b) broadband
3 desalinated   c) plastics
4 smart   d) station
5 3D   e) materials
6 satellite   f) trains
7 space   g) printing
8 wearable   h) water

3 ⭐ **Complete the sentences with phrases from exercise 2.**

1 Bottles and bags are more environmentally friendly if they are made of _____.
2 The most popular _____ are smart watches.
3 _____ is used to produce objects instead of documents.
4 In dry countries like Australia, many people drink _____.
5 The AVE is a _____ that connects cities in Spain including Madrid and Seville.
6 The International _____ is about 400km from Earth.

4 ⭐⭐ **Which inventions are these comments about?**

1 If I had one of these, I wouldn't need to pass my driving test! _____
2 My mum says she prefers the old-fashioned kind of books with pages to these. _____
3 The great thing about this is it doesn't break if you drop it. _____
4 If we have this, will it give us a faster internet connection? _____
5 Why would anyone want to go on a trip to Mars? _____
6 The frame of these glasses goes back to its original shape after bending it if you put it in hot water! _____

5 ⭐⭐⭐ **What would you do if you had these gadgets? Write full sentences.**

1 a 3D printer
   _____If I had a 3D printer I would ..._____
2 a flexible smartphone
   _____
3 a driverless car
   _____

Grammar
The passive

1 ★ Complete the sentences with the present simple passive form of the verbs in the box. Then match sentences 1–5 with pictures a–e.

carry   eat   fill   read   wear

1 This snack _____ at the cinema. ___
2 These _____ by athletes and many other people. ___
3 This _____ by people to protect them from the rain. ___
4 These _____ by people on paper and online. ___
5 This _____ with clothes that you want to take with you on a trip. ___

a   b   c   d   e

2 ★ Write sentences in the past simple passive.

The history of brushing our teeth.

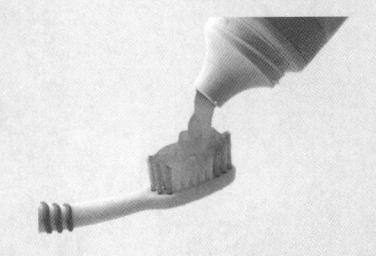

1 in ancient times / teeth / rub / with a twig / to clean them
_____

2 the first toothbrush / invent / in 1498 / in China
_____

3 it / make / from / hairs from a pig
_____

4 electric toothbrushes / not develop / until 1939 / in Switzerland
_____

5 toothpaste / use / in 500 BC / in China and India
_____

6 toothpaste in a tube / introduce / in the USA / in 1892 / by Dr Washington Sheffield
_____

3 ★★★ Complete the text with the correct passive form of the verbs in brackets.

The BIOME Car

This car, which (1) _____ (design) by Mercedes in 2010, is the most environmentally friendly car ever. First of all, it (2) _____ (not make), it (3) _____ (grow) from seeds! Secondly, it doesn't pollute the atmosphere. When it (4) _____ (drive), pure oxygen (5) _____ (produce)! Finally, at the end of their life, these cars (6) _____ (not throw) away. They (7) _____ (use) as building material for houses! Unfortunately, you can't buy them yet, but engineers believe that cars like these (8) _____ (produce) in about 20 years' time.

Copyright of Daimler AG.

4 ★★★ Write passive questions about the car in exercise 3 for these answers.

1 When _____? (it / design)
  In 2010.
2 How _____? (it / make)
  It's grown from seeds.
3 What _____ by the car? (produce)
  Pure oxygen.
4 Will _____ at the end of their life? (they / throw away)
  No.
5 What _____ for? (they / use)
  Building material.
6 When _____? (they / produce)
  In 20 years' time.

Vocabulary
Adverb review

1 ★ Match words 1–5 with definitions a–e.

1 quite
2 often
3 absolutely
4 rarely
5 quickly

a) completely
b) fast
c) not very often
d) not completely
e) frequently

2 ★★ Order the words to make sentences.

1 play / on / I / my phone / games /often / .
_____

2 app / absolutely / is / This / amazing / .
_____

3 competitors / All / talented / were / the / extremely / .
_____

4 on / always / Winston / Facebook / is / .
_____

5 solar oven / well / This / very / cooks / .
_____

6 for / Tablets /watching / useful / films / quite / are / .
_____

3 ★★ Tick (✓) the sentences that are correct. Correct the sentences that are wrong.

1 You can comfortable travel at 120 km per hour in this car. ☐
_____

2 Could you easy live without your mobile phone? ☐
_____

3 Jane talks so quiet that I can never hear what she's saying! ☐
_____

4 How fast can you find the answer to this question? ☐
_____

5 Matt always does good in science tests. ☐
_____

4 ★★ Complete the sentences with the correct form of the words in the box.

| good   happy   hard   incredible |
| safe   usual |

1 Most famous inventors worked _____ to come up with their ideas.

2 How _____ can a train travel at speeds of 350 km per hour?

3 My dad doesn't speak English very _____.

4 I don't _____ send text messages to my parents.

5 You have to be _____ intelligent to have an IQ of 150.

6 The astronauts waved _____ as they came out of the space shuttle.

5 ★★★ Complete the second sentence so that it has a similar meaning to the first. Use the correct form of the word in brackets.

1 The universe is very, very big! (absolute)
_____ enormous!

2 Why didn't you get here on time? (late)
Why _____?

3 I don't write letters to people very often. (rare)
I _____.

4 I've got a high speed internet connection. (quick)
I can connect to _____.

5 It isn't easy to play level 5 of this game. (quite)
It's _____.

Grammar
Active and passive voice

1 ⭐ **Are the sentences active or passive? Circle (A) or (P).**

1. Thousands of people download music from the internet every minute. A P
2. Lots of cool gadgets are invented by Japanese companies. A P
3. Will a robot with feelings be designed one day? A P
4. The flight attendant asked us to switch off our electronic devices. A P
5. This photo was sent from my smartphone. A P

2 ⭐ **Read the sentences and cross out the words in bold if they aren't necessary.**

1. Spanish is spoken **by 570 million people**.
2. Will a high-speed railway from China to the USA be built **by engineers** in the future?
3. The first affordable American cars were produced **by the Ford Motor Company**.
4. Eco-friendly crisp packets will soon be made from potatoes **by a British company**!
5. Over one billion hours of videos are watched **by YouTube users** every day!
6. Paper books are preferred **by people** who don't like reading on screen.

3 ⭐⭐ **Change the sentences from active to passive. Only include *by* if necessary.**

1. The Egyptians invented water clocks.
   Water clocks _____.
2. Pencil printers use old pencils instead of ink.
   Old pencils _____.
3. Someone might design an invisibility cloak like Harry Potter's one day.
   An invisibility cloak _____.
4. Russia sent the first dog into space in 1957.
   The first dog _____.
5. Amazon introduced the Kindle e-reader in 2007.
   The Kindle e-reader _____.

4 ⭐⭐⭐ **Complete the sentences with the correct active or passive form of the verbs in brackets.**

1. The TeenTech Awards _____ (aim) at 11–19-year-olds in the UK and Ireland.
2. They _____ (encourage) young people to use their creative skills to invent something new.
3. The best entries _____ (choose) by the judges later this year.
4. The awards ceremony _____ (hold) in London.
5. Last year's winners _____ (get) some great prizes!

5 ⭐⭐⭐ **Write active or passive questions for these answers.**

The electric bicycle

1. what / they / look like / ?
   _____
   They look like traditional bikes but with a motor and battery.
2. who / they / designed / for / ?
   _____
   They are made for people who want to get around quickly without sweating!
3. what / the other / benefits / ?
   _____
   As well as making journeys easier, they are cheaper than other forms of transport.
4. where / they / find / ?
   _____
   Although they can be bought in shops or online, e-bikes are also available to rent.
5. when / the electric bike / patented?
   _____
   The first electric bike was patented in 1881.

The boy who built windmills

When William Kamkwamba was growing up, none of the families in his village in Malawi had electricity in their houses. He was the youngest of seven children and his father was a farmer who **struggled** to grow enough food to feed his family. When William was 14, he had to leave school, but he was desperate to continue his education and spent all his time in the village library reading science books. Although he couldn't read English very well, he learned a lot from studying diagrams and pictures. He was already good at electronics as he had set up a small business **mending** radios for the people in the village, but now he was learning even more.

While he was studying a book about energy, William learned that it's possible to use the wind to make electricity. This gave him an idea: if he could build a windmill that could generate electricity to pump water, this could be used to **irrigate** his father's land and grow more food. It was difficult to find the building materials he needed and most people thought William was crazy as he spent all his free time searching through **scrapyards** begging for spare parts. Eventually, he managed to find almost everything and a friend bought him a bicycle-powered **generator**, the last part he needed.

William's first windmill made enough electricity for him to have a light in his bedroom. He was very happy to be able to read at night instead of going to bed as soon as it was dark. He immediately started work on a bigger, more powerful windmill using a bicycle frame and an old tractor fan. The big windmill not only generated electricity for the whole house, but it also powered a water pump for an irrigation system. As well as having electric light, the family could use the power at home for listening to radio – they no longer had to worry about **wearing out** the battery – and, eventually, watching TV.

The people who had laughed at William now came to the house so they could use his generator to recharge their mobile phones and radio batteries. People from the nearby villages came to visit too – at the time only 2% of people in the countryside in Malawi had electricity – and William soon became a local hero. He was invited to give a TED talk in Tanzania and eventually finish his education in America and become the engineer he dreamed of being.

Reading

1 Read and listen to the article. Number the events in the correct order 1–8. 🔊 16

    a) He searched scrapyards for the parts he needed to build a windmill. ___

    b) William's first windmill made enough electricity to light his bedroom. ___

    c) William had to stop going to school so he spent all day in the library reading science books. _1_

    d) The second, bigger windmill pumped water to irrigate the farm. ___

    e) William became a local hero and got invited to give a TED talk. ___

    f) A friend gave William a bicycle generator. ___

    g) He learned enough about electronics to start a radio repair business. ___

    h) He read about using the wind to make electricity. ___

2 Match the words in bold in the text with definitions 1–6.

   1 a place where old machines and cars are left and the parts of them are sold _____

   2 losing all its power or strength _____

   3 had a lot of difficulties while trying very hard to do something _____

   4 a machine that makes electricity _____

   5 bring water to a place so that plants can grow there _____

   6 fixing things that are broken or damaged _____

3 Read the text again and answer the questions.

   1 What did most people think about William's first windmill?

   2 How did people's attitudes towards William change after he built his second windmill?

   3 In what ways did people in the village benefit from William's windmill?

Listening

1 Listen to an interview about the TeenTech Awards. Which of the following subjects are represented at these awards? 🔊 17

- French ☐
- Science ☐
- Maths ☐
- Art ☐
- Technology ☐
- Geography ☐

2 Listen again. Circle T (true), F (false) or DS (doesn't say).

1. Anyone in the UK and Ireland can enter the TeenTech Awards. T F DS
2. The awards have over twenty categories. T F DS
3. Applicants work in groups of three. T F DS
4. The winners will be chosen by a panel of eight judges. T F DS
5. The winners receive a cash prize. T F DS

3 Answer the questions. Write full sentences.

1. What examples does Anna give of previous winning entries?
   _____
2. What are the winners invited to do in London?
   _____
3. What did 22% of applicants say they were interested in at the end of the competition?
   _____

Speaking

4 Complete the presentation with the phrases in the box. Listen and check. 🔊 18

> a few years   after   by the   in the
> it wasn't until   later

Today I'm going to talk to you about the history of the bicycle. It began in 1817 when the Running Machine was invented in Germany. You sat on it and the wheels helped you walk faster!

(1) _____ mid-1860s, the Boneshaker was introduced. It had pedals and was called the 'Boneshaker' because it was very uncomfortable to ride!

(2) _____ later, the high-wheeled bicycle became popular. It had rubber tyres, which made it more comfortable than the Boneshaker.

(3) _____ that, the Rover safety bicycle, which looked very similar to modern bicycles, was developed in England. However, (4) _____ 1888 that pneumatic tyres were invented. These were filled with air and made cycling even more comfortable.

When the car was invented, cycling lost popularity among adults. However, (5) _____ 1920s, bicycle manufacturers had started producing children's bicycles and they became the most popular toy ever!

And, (6) _____, cycling became a common leisure activity. This led to the design of racing bikes in the 1960s, followed by mountain bikes in the 1980s.

Writing

5 Imagine you have written this letter of complaint and complete 1–6.

(1) _____
_____
_____

The Manager
Technodream
269 Shore Street
London W2 4GD   9th May

Dear (2) _____ ,

On 3rd May I purchased a tablet (Fusion Tab 3 at £89.99) from your online shop. Although it was delivered on time, I was disappointed to discover that the camera does not work.

To (3) _____ situation, I would appreciate it if you could refund my money as quickly as possible.

I (4) _____ reply and a resolution to this problem.

(5) _____

(6) _____

Progress check

Vocabulary
Innovation and invention

1 Circle the correct words.

1. The world's longest **driverless car** / **high-speed train** line is in China.
2. These running shoes are made of **smart materials** / **wearable gadgets** that adapt to the shape of your foot.
3. You can store hundreds of digital books on a(n) **flexible smartphone** / **e-reader**.
4. Research is often carried out by astronauts on space **stations** / **tourism**.
5. **Satellite broadband** / **3D printing** is a cheap way of producing toys.
6. Many supermarkets now use food packaging made from **bioplastics** / **desalinated water**.

Adverb review

2 Tick (✓) the sentences that are correct. Correct the sentences that are wrong.

1. I was absolute furious when Jack used my new tablet without asking! ☐
_____
2. The air conditioning isn't working good and it's extremely hot. ☐
_____
3. My friends and I buy rarely CDs because they're expensive. ☐
_____
4. These questions are really easily! ☐
_____
5. Jess tried hard to fix her phone, but she couldn't. ☐
_____
6. My parents complain that I'm on always the computer! ☐
_____
7. Is there a simply way to learn a language? ☐
_____
8. Is the exam very hard? ☐
_____

Grammar
The passive

3 Complete the sentences with the correct passive form of the verbs in the box.

> create   find   invent   listen to
> not make   not use   play   speak

1. Mobile phones _____ by many people 20 years ago.
2. Today, a lot of waste _____ by mobile phones and other gadgets.
3. I hope cures _____ for all diseases one day.
4. Before the invention of CDs, music _____ on record players.
5. Now, music _____ on the internet by many people.
6. Do you think Mandarin _____ by everyone in 20 years' time?
7. The first trip to Mars _____ before 2030.
8. Ice cream _____ in the 16th century.

Active and passive voice

4 Complete the text with the correct active or passive form of the verbs in brackets.

The pot-in-a-pot fridge is a very ancient technology which (1)_____ (use) by the Ancient Egyptians as long ago as 2500 BCE. It is a simple but very effective way of keeping food cool and fresh in hot temperatures. You place your food into a pot which (2)_____ (put) inside a bigger pot. The bigger pot (3)_____ (fill) with wet sand and as the water in the sand (4)_____ (evaporate), this draws heat out of the smaller pot. This wonderfully cheap and simple technology (5)_____ (forget) when modern electric fridges (6)_____ (arrive) on the market; but it (7)_____ (rediscover) by a young man called Mohamed Bah Abba in Nigeria. He set up a business to produce pot-in-a-pot refrigerators for poor families in the desert and he (8)_____ (win) several awards for business innovation.

Extension

Cumulative vocabulary

1 Complete the sentences with the correct form of the word in CAPITALS.

The computer was small enough to fit ___comfortably___ into a coat pocket. COMFORT

1 She is interested in space _____ and wants to be an astronaut. EXPLORE
2 There were two _____ in the competition and it was difficult to choose the winner. FINAL
3 The young _____ demonstrated how his amazing machine works. INVENT
4 Don't worry if you haven't passed your driving test: _____ cars will soon be on the road! DRIVER
5 Scientists suggested a variety of different _____ to resolve this problem. SOLVE

2 Complete the second sentence so that it has a similar meaning to the first. Use the negative form of the word in brackets.

They can't wait to try the new software. (patient)
They are ___impatient___ to try the new software.

1 Atoms are so small that we can't see them. (visible)
Atoms are so small that they are _____.
2 Computers can't have original ideas. (possible)
It is _____ for computers to have original ideas.
3 Scientists probably won't find life on planet Mars. (likely)
It is _____ that scientists will find life on planet Mars.
4 The scientist was born with a physical problem, which meant he couldn't walk. (ability)
The scientist was born with a _____ which meant he couldn't walk.

More practice

> Grammar reference p92
> Advance your vocabulary p107
> Writing hub p120
> Phrase book pp148–149
> Wordlist pp151–157

Cumulative grammar

3 Circle the correct words.

A Russian scientist called Sergey Zimov (1) **is planning** / **is planned** to turn a national park in Siberia into a special pre-historic environment – as it was 1.2 million-years ago. The climate in this region is very cold: the ground (2) **covers** / **is covered** by snow for eight months of the year; not many plants or trees (3) **are grown** / **grow** in the frozen earth and there aren't many animals. If Zimov's project goes ahead, large animals (4) **will be introduced** / **are introduced** into the park environment like there (5) **were** / **have been** in prehistoric times.

Already, some deer, ponies and some wolves (6) **brought** / **have been brought** into the national park area. Zimov (7) **has studied** / **is studied** the land here for more than 30 years and (8) **has found** / **finds** the bones of all the different sorts of animals that lived there hundreds of thousands of years ago. He believes that if certain animals, particularly large grass-eating animals, (9) **have reintroduced** / **are reintroduced**, they (10) **will affect** / **affect** the environment in positive ways. They (11) **will eat** / **eat** the plants that cover the ground and this (12) **would help** / **will help** grass and trees to grow there again. Zimov thinks that when the large grass-eating animals (13) **were killed** / **have been killed** by humans, thousands of years ago, this (14) **is caused** / **caused** the environment to change.

The most exciting part of the plan is that scientists (15) **try** / **are trying** to clone a mammoth – the big, hairy elephant that (16) **would live** / **lived** in this area in the past. Zimov hopes that it (17) **has been** / **will be** possible to clone a mammoth from mammoth bones and to reintroduce them into the environment.

UNIT 6 YOUR IDENTITY

Vocabulary
Identity theft

1 ★ Match 1–4 with a–d.

1. internet
2. bank
3. junk
4. social networking

a) mail
b) site
c) scam
d) account

2 ★★ Complete the sentences with the words in the box.

credit   documents   loan   log   phishing

1. Lou's forgotten her username so she can't _____ on.
2. You should always shred _____ like bank statements that contain personal information.
3. Students in the UK often get a _____ to pay for their university expenses.
4. I got a _____ email asking me for my bank account number, but I deleted it.
5. You need a good _____ rating to borrow money from a bank.

3 ★★★ Match the words in the box with definitions 1–5.

credit card   debt   fraudster
spending spree   wi-fi hotspot

1. A person who tries to cheat others. _____
2. This is when you go shopping and buy lots of things. _____
3. You can use this instead of money to buy things. _____
4. A public place where you can use the internet. _____
5. Money that someone owes. _____

4 ★★ Complete the text with words from exercises 1–3.

Safety on the internet
How to protect yourself

- If you use a (1) _____ to buy something online, make sure you know the site you're buying from is safe.
- Be careful when using the internet in a (2) _____ because it's easier for someone to hack into your computer in a public place.
- Never arrange to meet a stranger who contacted you through a (3) _____. It's easy for users to create a fake profile and pretend to be someone they're not.
- If you use internet banking, never tell anyone your password because they could take money out of your (4) _____.
- If someone contacts you online asking you for your personal details, don't give them because the person might be a (5) _____.

5 ★★★ Answer the questions. Write full sentences.

1. What are the advantages of having a bank account?
   _____
2. Would you like to have your own credit card? Why (not)?
   _____
3. What did you buy the last time you went on a spending spree?
   _____
4. What information shouldn't you post on social networking sites?
   _____

Grammar
Modals of ability and possibility, obligation and prohibition

1 ⭐ Circle the correct words.

1 I **couldn't / mustn't** believe it when someone stole my purse.
2 We **had to / must** get up early yesterday.
3 You **can't / have to** use a credit card to pay your bus fare!
4 You **mustn't / don't have to** wear expensive clothes to look good.
5 I **didn't have to / mustn't** call Mike because he sent me a message.

2 ⭐ Rewrite the sentences in the past.

1 I can take money out of my bank account.
_____
2 You don't have to buy a smartphone!
_____
3 We must call the police.
_____
4 Dad can't remember his password.
_____
5 Harriet has to get a new passport.
_____

3 ⭐⭐ Complete the email with the words in the box.

> can   can't (x2)   couldn't
> had to   have to

Dear Ben,
Help! I (1) _____ find my mobile phone! I (2) _____ go to volleyball practice yesterday and I think it was in my bag, but when I got home I (3) _____ find it. At the moment I (4) _____ call you because your number is on my phone! I (5) _____ find it! Maybe I left it at your house. (6) _____ you please check?

Thanks,
Kate

4 ⭐⭐⭐ Complete the second sentence so it has a similar meaning to the first. Use the words in the box.

> ~~can't~~   don't have to   have to   mustn't

I've forgotten Claire's email address.
I can't remember Claire's email address.

1 It isn't necessary to be 18 to have a bank account.
You _____.
2 Don't tell anyone your password!
You _____!
3 You need to have a passport to travel abroad.
You _____.

5 ⭐⭐⭐ Choose the correct answers.

Boy didn't know he was using his dad's credit card to pay for game

A 12-year-old boy accidentally ran up a bill of £1,150 on his father's credit card while he was playing an online game. Sam Ghera (1) _____ believe it when his bank informed him that there was hardly any money in his account. He had given his son Nik his credit card details to pay the £5.99 monthly fee so he (2) _____ play the online game with his friends. Without his knowledge, however, he was being charged for an online currency that players (3) _____ choose to use to upgrade characters and other features of the game! Nik, who thought he was using game points that he'd won to improve the game, said he (4) _____ enter a password to make a purchase – all he (5) _____ do was click on the screen. His father says that online games companies (6) _____ make the hidden costs of playing such games clearer so that other parents don't end up with similar debts.

1 a) can't   b) couldn't   c) mustn't
2 a) could   b) can   c) had to
3 a) must   b) can't   c) can
4 a) mustn't   b) doesn't have to   c) didn't have to
5 a) had to   b) must   c) could
6 a) must to   b) have to   c) had to

Vocabulary
Personal identity

1 ★ Find 12 words related to personal identity in the wordsquare.

A	C	N	A	T	I	O	N	A	L	I	T	Y	I
P	E	V	O	R	S	U	W	P	E	R	L	L	E
P	R	E	L	A	T	I	O	N	S	H	I	P	Q
E	B	M	P	Y	Q	B	J	I	E	E	F	U	M
A	E	P	O	S	S	E	S	S	I	O	N	K	H
R	L	R	H	T	N	S	T	M	C	U	T	P	E
A	I	F	A	B	O	Y	Y	W	H	O	P	E	T
N	E	I	P	D	V	A	L	U	E	S	C	E	H
C	F	T	Z	O	Y	P	E	W	N	H	I	R	N
E	S	H	F	R	Q	E	I	J	M	A	Y	G	I
G	E	N	D	E	R	G	B	R	O	O	N	R	C
E	P	E	R	S	O	N	A	L	I	T	Y	O	I
P	F	W	D	O	T	X	G	U	R	L	M	U	T
F	R	I	E	N	D	S	H	I	P	X	I	P	Y

2 ★ Add the suffixes in the box to the root words to make nouns. Make any necessary changes to spelling.

-ance   -ity   -ment   -ness   -ship

1 appear _____
2 improve _____
3 citizen _____
4 happy _____
5 rely _____
6 sad _____
7 creative _____
8 entertain _____
9 ethnic _____
10 friend _____

3 ★★ Match questions 1–6 with subjects a–f.

1 Which country are you from? ___
2 Are you male or female? ___
3 What is important to you? ___
4 What do you look like? ___
5 What kind of clothes do you wear? ___
6 Who are the important people in your life? ___

a) appearance
b) relationships
c) gender
d) nationality
e) style
f) values

4 ★★ Read the definitions and complete the words.

1 people of the same age and background
  p_____ g_____
2 your nationality, language and cultural background are part of this   e_____
3 the relationship you have with a friend   f_____
4 the mixture of characteristics that makes someone different from others   p_____
5 a person's opinions   b_____
6 the things someone owns   p_____

5 ★★ Complete the information about the fashion blogger Tavi Gevinson.

Name: Tavi Gevinson
Date of birth: 21 April 1996
(1) _____: female
(2) _____: American
(3) _____: blond hair, blue eyes
(4) _____: confident, funny
(5) _____: individual
(6) _____: That people should be themselves and not copy others.

6 ★★★ Write a full sentence to describe …

1 your personality.
_____
2 your beliefs.
_____
3 your style.
_____
4 your favourite possession.
_____
5 a friendship or relationship that is important to you.
_____

Grammar
Modals of deduction

1 ⭐ **Order the words to make sentences.**

1 photo / selfie / must / Emma / of / That / a / be / .
   _____
2 a party / be / There / downstairs / might / .
   _____
3 a / language / be / Welsh / difficult / must / .
   _____
4 be / This / cheap / restaurant / can't / .
   _____
5 Chris / a profile / Facebook / have / could / on / .
   _____
6 not / His / work / might / laptop / old / .
   _____

2 ⭐ **Look at the pictures. Complete the sentences with *must* or *can't*.**

1 He _____ be frightened!
2 They _____ be twins. 
3 That _____ be you in the photo! 
4 That _____ be expensive 
5 She _____ be French. 

3 ⭐⭐ **Write sentences with *might* or *might not* and the verbs in brackets. In which sentences could the modal verb be replaced with *could*?**

1 Chloe _____ (eat) meat because her parents are vegetarians.
2 David hasn't arrived yet. The bus _____ (be) late.
3 It _____ (be) cold – I can see people outside wearing coats.
4 Dad _____ (let) me use his credit card because he doesn't trust me!
5 I want to play this game because it _____ (be) fun – Chris enjoyed it.

4 ⭐⭐⭐ **Rewrite the sentences using the words in the box.**

   can't   might   might not   must

1 It's possible that they're on holiday.
   _____
2 I'm sure it's Eve's birthday today.
   _____
3 It's possible that Jenny won't like the photo.
   _____
4 I'm sure that the boy in the café isn't Dylan.
   _____

5 ⭐⭐⭐ **Complete the sentences about the people in the picture. Use the words in brackets and modals of deduction with the verb *be*.**

1 _____ because they look similar. (sisters)
2 _____ because they're smiling. (happy)
3 _____ because they're wearing school uniforms. (university students)
4 _____ because the Eiffel Tower is in the background. (in Paris)
5 _____ because they aren't wearing coats. (summer)

51

| Home | New | Sports | Culture | Business | Lifestyle |

When the person behind your Facebook profile isn't you!

Rachel Sterling was horrified to find messages chatting to her friends on Facebook which she had not written. The teenager had recently lost her mobile phone – it was stolen from her bag while she was swimming – and now the thief was pretending to be her.

Nowadays, there are more and more cases of people impersonating others on social networking sites, otherwise known as 'e-personation'. In Rachel's case, the imposter turned out to be a jealous classmate. She changed Rachel's passwords – locking her out of her Facebook account, email and Snapchat – and posted aggressive comments and messages to upset Rachel's friends and family for months before she was caught.

It isn't just teenagers who are at risk. Celebrities are often targets of online impersonation too. After several fans approached him after shows demanding to know why he had stopped chatting with them on Facebook, Kip Moore, an American country music singer discovered that there were several accounts impersonating him on Facebook and Instagram. The accounts sent messages to his fans asking them to donate money to a charity which didn't really exist.

To investigate the problem, *New York Times* newspaper researched fake social media accounts for the ten most followed people on Instagram. Taylor Swift had 233 impersonators and Beyoncé had 714, but the Brazilian football player Neymar had the biggest problem. They found 1,676 accounts in his name across Facebook, Instagram and Twitter.

Internet imposters may have personal reasons to target their victim or they just want money but they usually use one of two methods. They either create a new profile in the other person's name, as in the cases above, or hack into someone's social media account, changing the password so the true owner can no longer access it. The good news is that it is going to become easier to prosecute 'e-personators' in the future. 'E-personation' is becoming a crime in many countries – punished by a fine or even a prison sentence.

In the meantime, there are some steps you can take to avoid being a victim of this kind of crime. First of all, create unusual passwords for your social media accounts that are impossible for a stranger to guess. Secondly, be very careful about revealing personal information about yourself online. The more internet imposters know about you, the easier it is for them to pretend to be you!

Reading

1 Read and listen to the article. What is it about? 🔊 19

   a) Some internet crimes that have never been solved.
   b) People who trick others on the internet.
   c) The methods used to catch online criminals.

2 Read the text again. Choose the correct answers.

  1 The messages on Rachel Sterling's Facebook page were written by …
    a) a stranger.
    b) someone Rachel knew.
  2 'E-personation' is a crime which involves …
    a) locking another person out of their social media accounts.
    b) pretending to be another person using the internet.
  3 Someone created a profile in Kip Moore's name …
    a) in order to cheat his fans.
    b) in order to raise money for a charity.
  4 The reason for committing this kind of crime …
    a) varies from person to person.
    b) is usually to get money.
  5 In the future, if you impersonate someone online …
    a) you could face punishment.
    b) you are very likely to be caught.
  6 According to the article, you can protect yourself against 'e-personation' by …
    a) frequently changing your password to social networking sites.
    b) giving very few details about yourself when using social networking sites.

LIFELONG LEARNING STRATEGY

Questions often express key information from the text in different words. Check your answers in exercise 2, by underlining the words or phrases in the text which helped you choose the answers.

Listening

1 Listen to a radio programme about TCKs. What do the letters TCK stand for? 20
_____

2 Listen again. Choose the correct answers.

1 The teenagers where Liam used to live …
   a) didn't play basketball.
   b) loved football.
   c) used to go to barbeques a lot.
2 How many languages can Jiya speak?
   a) three
   b) four
   c) six
3 People like Jiya and Liam usually …
   a) get on well with other TCKs.
   b) find it hard to identify with other people.
   c) wish they could always live in the same place.
4 The organization Jiya describes is for …
   a) young people only.
   b) adults only.
   c) people of all ages.

3 Answer the questions.

1 How old was Liam when he went to live in Mexico?
_____
2 What two adjectives do people sometimes use to describe Jiya?
_____
3 When was the TCK organization started?
_____
4 How many members has it got?
_____

Speaking

4 Match sentence beginnings 1–5 with endings a–e to make phrases used for giving counter-arguments.

1 That's not how I   a) it like that at all.
2 I see   b) see it.
3 I don't see   c) disagree completely.
4 I'm afraid I don't   d) things differently.
5 Sorry, but I   e) agree.

5 Read part of a debate about body art. Then complete it with the phrases from exercise 4. Listen and check. 21

Seb: I think it's wrong to change your appearance by having things like piercings and tattoos.
Cait: I'm (1) _____. Body art can be really attractive.
Seb: That's (2) _____.
I understand that people might get bored with their appearance, but can't they just change their hair colour? Why do they have to have permanent images printed on their bodies or holes in their ears or nose?
Cait: I'm sorry, (3) _____. I've got pierced ears and I think they look great. Everyone has the right to do whatever they want with their bodies.
Seb: I don't (4) _____. I mean you might like them now, but what about in 50 years' time? You might wish you hadn't got holes in your ears then!
Cait: Well, you've made some interesting points, but (5) I _____.
I guess we'll just have to agree to disagree!

Writing

6 Circle the correct words.

1 My passport was stolen **because** / **so** I couldn't go on holiday.
2 Many teenagers don't like using Facebook **because** / **because of** their parents are on it!
3 My dad saw a TV programme about internet fraud. **As a result,** / **Due to** he never buys anything online.
4 Anna can speak Portuguese fluently **because** / **due to** the fact that her father is Brazilian.
5 Someone has tried unsuccessfully to hack into your email account. We **because of** / **therefore** recommend that you change your password immediately.
6 **As a result** / **Because of** his own experience as a fraudster, Frank Abagnale has a lot of knowledge about how scams work.

Progress check

Vocabulary
Identity theft

1 Circle the correct words.

1. Is this café a **junk** / **wi-fi** hotspot?
2. My mum paid for the shoes with her credit **account** / **card**.
3. Banks don't give **debts** / **loans** to teenagers!
4. Don't **shred** / **log on** those documents because I need them!
5. Amy's got some money so she's going on a **spending** / **phishing** spree.
6. The woman seemed nice and friendly, but she was actually a **scam** / **fraudster**.
7. Instagram is my favourite social **rating** / **networking** site.

Personal identity

2 Complete the sentences with the words in the box.

> appearance   beliefs   ethnicities
> friendship   gender   nationality
> peer   personality   relationship
> style   values

1. My parents have taught me many important _____.
2. Girls shouldn't be treated differently from boys just because of their _____.
3. I have a good _____ with my dad, but we sometimes argue!
4. Would you ever have plastic surgery to improve your _____?
5. My mum is from France, but she also has Spanish _____.
6. Lady Gaga doesn't follow fashion – she's got her own _____!
7. For my _____ group, the internet is a big part of our everyday lives.
8. Paula looks like her sister, but she's got a completely different _____.
9. I've known Owen for years and our _____ is very important to me.
10. There's an interesting mix of cultures and _____ in this city.
11. You don't have to give details about your religious _____ on your passport.

Grammar
Modals of ability and possibility, obligation and prohibition

3 Complete the sentences with a suitable modal verb. Use the affirmative or negative form.

1. I _____ tell my parents I'll be back late tonight or they'll be worried about me.
2. Most social media sites are free – you _____ pay to use them.
3. I looked for that website you told me about but I _____ find it.
4. My brother broke the camera on my phone and now I _____ take photos.
5. You _____ buy a new camera quite cheaply on Amazon.
6. The teacher's computer stopped working so he _____ get a new one.
7. If they spoke slowly and clearly we _____ understand what they said.
8. You _____ share your personal information with strangers.
9. In the past, we _____ change our passwords so often, but now you need to change them every month.

Modals of deduction

4 Circle the correct words.

1. Paul **must** / **can** be on holiday – I haven't seen him for a few days.
2. That boy **could** / **must** be Jenny's brother, but I'm not sure.
3. The party **could** / **might** not start until 9pm because nobody is here yet!
4. Being a private detective **can** / **must** be a very interesting job.
5. You **can** / **must** be Natalie! It's nice to meet you!
6. Those **mustn't** / **can't** be Philip's shoes because they're too small!

Extension

UNIT 6

Cumulative vocabulary

1 Complete the sentences with a word from box A and a word from box B.

A
credit   digital   disable   fake   privacy
~~spread~~   phishing   screen   site

B
administrator   cookies   grab   footprint
news   scam   rating   ~~rumours~~   settings

They never make unkind comments or <u>spread rumours</u> about people online.

1 There's too much _____ _____ on social media: I always check facts on a proper news site.
2 It's a good idea to check your _____ _____ online if you want to borrow money from the bank.
3 There's a _____ _____ where people ring up pretending there's a problem with your internet and ask you for your passwords.
4 I found some pictures of me on Instagram that I didn't like so I contacted the _____ _____ to get them taken down.
5 Your _____ _____ is how you present yourself on the internet and you add to it each time you go online.
6 She changed her _____ _____ so that now only her friends can see her photos.
7 It's possible to take a _____ _____ from anyone's social media site and paste it somewhere else.
8 If you want to have more online privacy, make sure you _____ the _____ on your browser.

More practice
> Grammar reference p94
> Advance your vocabulary p108
> Writing hub p122
> Phrase book pp148–149
> Wordlist pp151–157

Cumulative grammar

2 Choose the correct answers.

Joe: I (1) _____ for you on Facebook last night, but I (2) _____ find you.
Sofia: That's because I'm not on it!
Joe: But you used (3) _____ Facebook!
Sofia: I know, but then a friend of mine (4) _____ me about Heyu.
Joe: What's Heyu? I (5) _____ of it.
Sofia: I (6) _____ heard of it before either, it's a new social media app for teenagers!
Joe: Really? Is it like Facebook?
Sofia: A bit. You (7) _____ do most of the same things, but there aren't any adverts.
Joe: That (8) _____ be great!
Sofia: Yes, it is. Heyu users can also send instant messages from their phones and they (9) _____ pay for them.
Joe: Wow! If I'd known about Heyu before, I (10) _____ !
Sofia: You don't join Heyu. You (11) _____ to become a member by another member.
Joe: OK. (12) _____ going to invite me, then?
Sofia: No way!
Joe: Why not?
Sofia: I (13) _____ ! What's your email address?

	a)	b)	c)
1	've looked	was looking	had looked
2	might not	can't	couldn't
3	love	to love	loving
4	told	tells	has told
5	never have heard	've never heard	didn't never hear
6	hadn't	didn't	haven't
7	could	would	can
8	must	had to	will
9	have not to	don't have to	mustn't
10	will join	would join	would have joined
11	invite	're invited	're inviting
12	You	Will you	Are you
13	joke	joking	'm joking

UNIT 7 THAT'S ENTERTAINMENT

Vocabulary
Film-making

1 ★ Label the photos with the words in the box.

> camera operator   storyboard
> costume designer   lighting
> soundtrack   make-up artist
> script   set designer

1 _____
2 _____ 
3 _____ 
4 _____ 
5 _____ 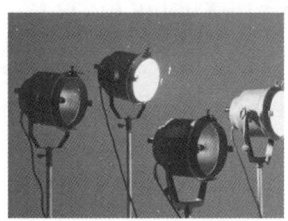
6 _____ 
7 _____ 
8 _____ 

2 ★ Match sentences 1–6 with the words in the box.

> cast   credits   crew   locations
> sound effects   subtitles

1 They filmed it in Edinburgh and Paris. _____
2 It was in French, but it was translated into English. _____
3 The actors were all unknown. _____
4 The people who worked on the film were French. _____
5 The noises in the battle scenes were very realistic. _____
6 Did you read the list of people who worked on the film? _____

3 ★★ The words in bold are incorrect. Write the correct words.

1 The **crew** usually appear at the end of a film. _____
2 Lunch was provided for all members of the cast and **credits**. _____
3 The **subtitles** were so loud that they gave me a headache! _____
4 The **set designer** stops filming when the director says 'Cut!'. _____
5 Mum wasn't wearing her glasses so she couldn't read the **sound effects**. _____

4 ★★★ Complete the sentences so they are true for you.

1 The best film I've seen recently is _____.
2 I liked it because _____.
3 If I could work on a film, I'd like to be a(n) _____ because _____.

Grammar
Reported speech

1 ⭐ Circle the correct words.

1 Emily said that she **'s enjoyed / 'd enjoyed** the film.
2 It was late and the crew said they **'d felt / were feeling** tired.
3 The teacher said we **had / have had** to learn our lines for the play by Friday.
4 After shouting at me, Matt said he **'s / was** sorry.
5 The director said they **will / would** finish filming the next day.
6 The make-up artist said I **can't / couldn't** use my phone while she was doing my make-up.

2 ⭐ Order the words to make sentences in reported speech.

1 said / wanted / Bea / play / she /starring role / the / to / .
　_____
2 everyone / Nigel / made coffee / 'd /said /for / he / .
　_____
3 be / The producer / 'd / I / a star / said / !
　_____
4 understand / couldn't / she / the film / said / Maria / .
　_____
5 wasn't / well / The actor / feeling / he / said / .
　_____

3 ⭐⭐ Rewrite the direct speech as reported speech.

　'You have talent!'
　My drama teacher said that _I had talent_ .
1 'My name is Bond.'
　The man said that _____ .
2 'I haven't seen that film.'
　Troy said that _____ .
3 'We're starting a film club.'
　The students said that _____ .
4 'You must be home by ten o'clock!'
　Dad said that _____ .
5 'I can't remember the title of the movie.'
　Sadie said that _____ .
6 'I'm sorry I didn't call you yesterday.'
　Max said that _____ .

4 ⭐⭐⭐ Write what the people say.

> Maggie said Jack was late. Jack said he had missed the bus. Maggie said they couldn't go to the cinema now. She said the film had already started. Jack said it didn't matter. He said they didn't have to go to the cinema. He said he was feeling hungry. Maggie said that luckily she knew a nice café near the cinema.

　　'You're late!' , said Maggie.
1 _____ , said Jack.
2 _____ , Maggie said.
3 _____ , she said.
4 _____ , Jack said.
5 _____ , he said.
6 _____ , he said.
7 _____ , Maggie said.

5 ⭐⭐⭐ Read the text message and complete the paragraph to report what Claire says.

> 12:01
> Dear Jess,
> I'm really excited! I was on my way home when I saw some people making a film. I recognized one of the actors. I've seen him on TV before, but I can't remember his name. I'm going to call Natalie to tell her. She'll be very jealous!
> Claire ☺

Claire said that she (1) _was really excited_ . She said she (2) _____ on her way home when she (3) _____ some people making a film. She said she (4) _____ one of the actors. She said that she (5) _____ him on TV before, but that she (6) _____ his name. She said she (7) _____ Natalie to tell her and that she (8) _____ very jealous.

Vocabulary
Reporting verbs

1 ⭐ Match sentences 1–6 with verbs a–f.

1 'I lied to you!' ___
2 'This film is so boring!' ___
3 'Let's meet for a coffee later.' ___
4 'Will you come to my party?' ___
5 'I'll lend you ten euros if you want.' ___
6 'You're right!' ___

a) invite
b) offer
c) complain
d) agree
e) admit
f) suggest

2 ⭐ Complete the table with the headings in the box.

verb + *that*   verb + infinitive with *to*
verb + object + infinitive with *to*

1 _____	2 _____	3 _____
agree	ask	admit
offer	convince	complain
promise	invite	say
refuse	tell	suggest

3 ⭐⭐ Complete the sentences with the correct form of the verbs in brackets.

1 Mum agreed _____ (give) us a lift to the concert.
2 Bea complained that the film _____ (be) too long.
3 I refused _____ (wear) a pink dress to the birthday party.
4 Sean suggested that we _____ (take) a photo of ourselves.
5 My friends convinced me _____ (not tell) my parents.
6 Helen admitted that she _____ (not like) the CD I lent her.
7 Dad promised _____ (buy) me a new phone.
8 A woman asked us _____ (not talk) in the cinema!

4 ⭐⭐⭐ Rewrite the sentences in reported speech using the verbs in the box.

admit   complain   offer
promise   refuse   suggest

1 'Yes, I sent the message!' said Sally.
  Sally _____.
2 'I'll love you forever!' said Mark to Bridget.
  Mark _____.
3 'I don't want to go to the party with you,' said Pippa to Oliver.
  Pippa _____.
4 'I'll pay for the tickets' said my aunt.
  My aunt _____.
5 'Let's watch this DVD!' said Nick.
  Nick _____.
6 'The people in front of me are too noisy!' said Georgia.
  Georgia _____.

5 ⭐⭐⭐ Complete the sentences so they are true for you.

1 I've promised _____.
2 One of my friends has invited me _____.
3 At restaurants, people sometimes complain _____.
4 I like watching films about _____ but I refuse _____.
5 When I go out with my friends, my parents usually ask me _____.

Grammar
Reported questions

1 ⭐ Order the words to complete the reported questions.

Last night, I watched an interview on TV with my favourite film star. First, the interviewer asked him (1) _____ (he / become / an / why / 'd / actor). Then she asked him (2) _____ (liked / famous / being / he / if). Next, she asked him (3) _____ (making / if / was / he / film / a) at that time. He said 'yes' and that he was playing the villain! Finally, she asked him (4) _____ (ever / 'd / he / Spain / visited / if) and he said 'no', so she asked him (5) _____ (travel / was / to / when / going / he / there)!

2 ⭐ Circle the correct words.

1 The woman asked me if I **was** / **'m** 18.
2 The teacher asked us why we **are** / **were** making so much noise.
3 Katie asked her mum if she **can** / **could** go to the festival.
4 My brother asked me how many friends I **had** / **was having** on Facebook.
5 Rob asked his dad when he **was** / **had been** a singer.

3 ⭐⭐ Write the reported questions in exercise 2 in direct speech.

1 _____
2 _____
3 _____
4 _____
5 _____

4 ⭐⭐ Complete the reported questions.

1 'What did you do last night?'
  Dad asked me what I _____ the night before.
2 'Were you with Suzie?'
  He asked me if I _____ with Suzie.
3 'Where did you go?'
  He asked me where we _____.
4 'Are you going out tonight?'
  He asked me if I _____ out that night.
5 'What time will you be back?'
  Finally, he asked me what time I _____ back.

5 ⭐⭐⭐ Read the speech bubbles and complete the text using reported speech.

1 How old are you?
2 Have you acted before?
3 Can you sing?
4 Which part are you interested in?
5 What's your phone number?

Yesterday I went for an audition to be in a theatre production of *High School Musical*. First, the director asked me (1) _____. Then she asked me (2) _____ and (3) _____.

After that, I had to read a bit of the script to her and she asked me (4) _____. Finally, she asked me (5) _____. I hope she'll call me!

So you want to make your own movie?

Nowadays, plenty of teenagers are making short films for YouTube – it's not as difficult as you might think! Follow film student Ben Hardy's advice about how to get started.

1 **Study films you like**
Pick one of your favourite movies and watch it with the sound turned off. Look closely at the **camera angles** and the lighting. You should also try watching short films on the internet to see how they manage to tell a complete story in just a few minutes.

2 **Work with what you've got**
It's a **myth** that you need a huge **budget** to make a film. With today's technology, you can even **shoot** and edit a film on a smartphone! Borrow costumes, **props** and anything else you need. Your friends will hopefully agree to be the cast. What about the scriptwriter, director and camera operator? You'll probably have to do these jobs!

3 **Get the technical details right**
Even if you've got a great script and cast, the film won't work if it's difficult to see or hear what's going on.

Learn how to use a camera properly and make sure the sound is good quality. If this isn't one of your strong points, then keep it simple and make a silent movie.

4 **Use real-life experiences**
Emily Hagins, who wrote and directed her first film when she was 12, often uses her own experiences in her films. For example, in *My Sucky Teen Romance*, one character, Kate, talks about **sweating** in front of a boy she likes. While this was an embarrassing experience for Emily in real life it was good material for the movie!

5 **Don't give up!**
The first film you make definitely won't be your best, but don't worry. The only way to learn the art of film-making is by making mistakes. Keep trying and you'll improve!

Reading

1 Read and listen to the article. Who do you think it was written for?))) 22

a) experienced film-makers
b) young cinema lovers
c) people who want to become film directors

2 Match the words in bold in the text with definitions 1–6.

1 something that isn't true _____
2 positions from which something is filmed _____
3 record a film _____
4 this happens when your body gets hot _____
5 objects used in a film _____
6 the amount of money you have to spend on something _____

3 Read the article again. Complete the sentences.

1 When you study a film that you like, you should focus on _____.
2 Some people wrongly believe that to make a film _____.
3 It isn't necessary to buy lots of equipment because you _____.
4 In her film scripts, Emily Hagins sometimes writes about _____.
5 You will only improve as a film maker if you _____.

4 Answer the questions. Write full sentences.

1 Who is Ben Hardy?
2 What do some short films do successfully in just a few minutes?
3 How can your friends help you make a film?
4 Who is Kate?

Listening

1 You are going to hear five people talking about their jobs. Look at the list of jobs (a–g) in exercise 2. What have they all got in common?

LIFELONG LEARNING STRATEGY

Understand why you are listening

Before you start listening, read the questions carefully so that you know exactly what information you are listening for. This will help you to decide what to focus on when you listen.

Look at exercise 2. What type of information are you listening for?

a) general information, eg the main idea
b) specific information, eg names, numbers, etc

If you are listening for general information, think about the context – who is speaking and why?

If you are listening for specific information, try to identify key words which will help you to find the answers.

2 Listen and match speakers 1–5 with five of the jobs a–g. 🔊 23

Speaker 1	a) costume designer
Speaker 2	b) extra
Speaker 3	c) scriptwriter
Speaker 4	d) actor
Speaker 5	e) set designer
	f) make-up artist
	g) camera operator

3 Listen again. Who says these things about their job? Write the numbers of the speakers.

1 I need to know about specific aspects of history. __
2 It sometimes takes a long time to achieve results. __, __
3 It isn't as interesting as people think. __
4 I sometimes take risks. __
5 I follow the instructions I'm given. __

Speaking

4 Circle the correct words. Listen and check. 🔊 24

Lucy: Hi. I'm doing some research (1) **into / of** teenagers' spending on entertainment. Could I ask (2) **to you / you** a few questions?
Seb: Er, OK. Will it take long?
Lucy: No, it won't take (3) **long / longer** than five minutes. I'll be (4) **taking / doing** notes – is that OK?
Seb: Sure.
Lucy: OK, let's get (5) **starting / started**! Can you (6) **tell me / tell** how much money you spend on entertainment a month?
Seb: About £40 a month.
Lucy: Right. Would you mind (7) **telling / to tell** me how you pay for it?
Seb: With my pocket money.
Lucy: I see. Do you ever go to concerts?
Seb: Not very often – and only if they're free!
Lucy: OK. Is there anything else (8) **you'll / you'd** like to add?
Seb: No, I don't think so.
Lucy: Great. Thank you so much (9) **for / to** taking part.

Writing

5 Rewrite the sentences using the words in the box.

> majority   more than half
> large proportion   ~~9 out of 10~~   10%

90% of teenagers own a mobile phone.
9 out of 10 teenagers own a mobile phone.

1 One in ten teenagers has their own tablet.
   _____

2 Most Hollywood stars are paid lots of money.
   _____

3 A lot of the music on MySpace is by unknown musicians.
   _____

4 Over 50% of the students at my school never go to the theatre.
   _____

Progress check

Vocabulary
Film-making

1 Match the words in the box with the definitions 1–10.

> camera operator   cast   costume designer
> credits   crew   location   script
> soundtrack   storyboard   subtitles

1 the list of people who work on a film _____
2 the place outside the studio where the film is shot _____
3 the music that is played during a film _____
4 the people who act in a film _____
5 a translation of the dialogue that appears on screen _____
6 the person who films the action _____
7 the person who makes the actors' clothes _____
8 the written dialogue of a film _____
9 the people who work behind the scenes on a film _____
10 a series of pictures showing the different scenes of a film _____

Reporting verbs

2 Circle the correct words.

1 George has **offered** / **invited** me to go to the film festival.
2 Can you **say** / **tell** me who this actor is?
3 I **complain** / **admit** that I don't always keep my promises!
4 Unfortunately, my parents **agree** / **refuse** to let me watch that programme.
5 How can I **convince** / **suggest** you that I'm telling the truth?
6 The director is going to **ask** / **promise** Emma to be in the film.

Grammar
Reported speech

3 Write the time expressions in reported speech.

1 today _____
2 yesterday _____
3 tomorrow _____
4 last week _____
5 next year _____
6 three months ago _____

4 Rewrite the sentences using reported speech.

1 'I love this song!'
  Ellie said _____.
2 'I'm going to be the DJ at the party.'
  Daniel said _____.
3 'I don't want to sit here.'
  Lara said _____.
4 'Steven Spielberg directed this film.'
  Tom said _____.
5 'You must see Veronica Mars!'
  My brother said _____.
6 'I'll rent these DVDs.'
  Maria said _____.
7 'I'm flying to Hollywood tomorrow!'
  Chloe said _____.
8 'I'll meet you here at nine o'clock.'
  Dan said _____.

Reported questions

5 Rewrite the questions using reported speech.

1 'When will the DVDs be available?' the woman asked.
  _____
2 'Is Ryan a good actor?' the producer asked her.
  _____
3 'Are you filming outside today?' Francis asked.
  _____
4 'How much does it cost to do the residential course?' Lee asked.
  _____
5 'Where can we find out about the film club?' the students asked.
  _____
6 'Did you recognize the last piece of music?' I asked Finn.
  _____

Extension

Cumulative vocabulary

1 Complete the text with the words in the box

> cast   characters   effects   gadgets
> kidnappings   location   secret agent
> shot   spies   stunts

The films about the adventures of a British (1) _____ called James Bond have been popular throughout the world for more than 50 years. The (2) _____ are based on the novels of the writer Ian Fleming and have not changed much over the years although the (3) _____ of actors has. A new James Bond replaces the previous one every few years, for example! The films are exciting and are (4) _____ in different, beautiful places all over the world. The stories are full of action with (5) _____ stealing secrets, (6) _____ of important people and rescue missions. Each film promises lots of action (7) _____ with James Bond flying planes, chasing people on skis or jumping off tall buildings. There are always car chases, fights and lots of special (8) _____ and Bond always uses some kind of amazing electronic (9) _____ to get everyone out of trouble and, most importantly of all, he always wins. Another thing that never changes in James Bond films: whenever we see him – on (10) _____ in the jungle or dining in the Ritz – agent 007 is always well dressed.

Cumulative grammar

2 Complete the text with the correct form of the verbs in brackets.

The popcorn seller who wrote a Hollywood film script

Even since he (1) _____ (be) a child, Stuart Gallop (2) _____ (love) the cinema, but he never dreamed that he would one day write the script for a Hollywood movie. As a teenager, Gallop, who (3) _____ (be) from Bristol in the UK, (4) _____ (use to) sell popcorn at his local cinema and enjoyed watching people's reactions after they (5) _____ (see) a good film. He said this experience (6) _____ (inspire) him to come up with his own idea for a movie.

Gallop started writing his script in his spare time while he (7) _____ (work) for a student accommodation company. He spent ten years working on the script, but only decided (8) _____ (try) and sell it to a film company when he lost his job. At the Cannes Film Festival, which (9) _____ (attract) some of the biggest names in the film industry every year, Gallop (10) _____ (meet) Hollywood film producers Beau Nelson and Kayo Anderson. The working title for his film was *In War They Come* and it (11) _____ (describe) in Gallop's notes as 'a sci-fi/action picture' about a group of aliens who come to Earth to kidnap human soldiers. They must (12) _____ (be) impressed with his script because after (13) _____ (read) it, they convinced investors (14) _____ (come up) with 10 million dollars to turn it into a movie!

More practice

- Grammar reference p96
- Advance your vocabulary p109
- Writing hub p124
- Phrase book pp148–149
- Wordlist pp151–157

UNIT 8 PERSUADING PEOPLE

Vocabulary
Advertising

1 ⭐ **Circle the correct words.**

1 Never believe the **target audience / hype** about a product until you actually try it.
2 Let's try a different **brand / advert** of breakfast cereal for a change!
3 This video of a cat singing has gone **viral / persuasive**!
4 There's a lot of **celebrity / peer pressure** among teenagers to have the right gadgets and clothes.
5 I find **jingles / online ads** annoying so I never click on them.
6 The company's new **ad agency / advertising campaign** is aimed at teens.
7 The **eye-catching / consumer** Turbo 101 is one of the biggest-selling tablets on the market.

2 ⭐⭐ **Match the definitions with words from Exercise 1.**

1 the influence that people of your age have on you   _____
2 noticeable because it is attractive or unusual   _____
3 a planned series of posters, adverts and events used to advertise something   _____
4 adverts on the internet   _____
5 a business which creates adverts for other companies   _____
6 the people that an advert is aimed at   _____

3 ⭐⭐ **Complete the text with the words in the box.**

> advert   brand   campaign   eye-catching
> online ads   target audience   viral

What makes a good (1) _____ ? First, it has to be (2) _____ in order to get the attention of the (3) _____ , but there's a lot more to it than that. Take two recent (4) _____ , which both went (5) _____ on YouTube. One shows an orangutan dancing crazily after drinking some of its favourite (6) _____ of orange juice. The other, which was part of an advertising (7) _____ for the Winter Olympics, shows scenes of mothers helping their children train to become athletes. Like any good movie, they both tell a story and make us laugh or cry (or both).

4 ⭐⭐ **Complete the questions with the words and phrases in the box.**

> ad agency   brand   gone viral
> peer pressure

1 Would you like to work in a(n) _____ ? Why (not)?
2 Do you ever feel _____ to buy the same things as your friends? If so, when?
3 What _____ of clothes is most popular with teenagers in your country?
4 Can you think of any online ads that have _____ in your country recently?

5 ⭐⭐⭐ **Answer the questions in exercise 4. Write full sentences.**

1 _____
2 _____
3 _____
4 _____

Grammar
Relative pronouns

1 ⭐ **Circle the correct words.**

1 Kate Moss is a model **whose** / **who's** appeared in adverts for clothes and perfume.
2 Do you know **whose** / **who's** husband that actor is?
3 Prada is a fashion brand **whose** / **who's** clothes are often worn by celebrities.
4 Paul Pogba is a French footballer **whose** / **who's** famous for his style.

2 ⭐⭐ **Complete the sentences with *who*, *which*, *when* or *where*. In which sentences could you replace your answers with *that*?**

1 Zara is a company _____ spends very little on advertising.
2 I can't remember the name of the shop _____ I bought this watch.
3 1742 was the year _____ the first advert appeared in a magazine.
4 Rob Janoff is the person _____ designed the logo for Apple computers.
5 Instagram is a site _____ you can share photos and videos.
6 *Teen Vogue* is a magazine _____ is aimed at teenage girls.

3 ⭐⭐⭐ **Join the sentences using the relative pronouns in the box.**

> where   which (x2)   who   whose

1 Starbucks is an American company. It has branches all over the world.
  _____
2 IKEA is a shop. You can buy things for the home there.
  _____
3 Fashion bloggers are people. They write about different fashion brands.
  _____
4 This is an advert. It has a cute puppy in it!
  _____
5 Oxfam is a charity. Its aim is to help people in need.
  _____

Indefinite pronouns

4 ⭐ **Circle the correct words.**

1 I can't remember **anything** / **something** about that film.
2 There must be **anywhere** / **somewhere** in Scotland where we could stay.
3 **Anyone** / **No one** remembered to buy my favourite biscuits!
4 I don't go **nowhere** / **anywhere** without my watch.
5 Does **someone** / **anyone** really take any notice of adverts?

5 ⭐⭐ **Complete the conversation with the words in the box.**

> anything   anywhere   no one   nothing
> someone   something

Finn: Advertising is (1) _____ that really gets on my nerves!
Amy: Why?
Finn: Because there's no escape from it! You can't go (2) _____ or do (3) _____ without seeing adverts.
Amy: I know, but (4) _____ makes you read them. You can just ignore them if you want.
Finn: How? They pop up whenever I'm online! Advertisers seem to think I've got (5) _____ better to do than read about products I don't want.
Amy: Talking of adverts, (6) _____ told me about a really funny one about a cat that wants to be a superhero. Have you seen it?
Finn: No!

6 ⭐⭐⭐ **Write a full sentence about …**

1 an advert that you like.
  _____
2 an advert that you hate.
  _____
3 someone who influences you.
  _____
4 something which you would really like to buy.
  _____

Vocabulary
Easily confused verbs

1 ⭐ Order the letters to make verbs used with *money*. Which two of the verbs can also be used with *time*?

1. nepsd _____
2. stawe _____
3. niw _____
4. rena _____
5. neld _____
6. rowbro _____

2 ⭐⭐ Complete the sentences with the words in the box.

> hope   remember   remind   see
> wait   watch

1. Mum doesn't let me _____ TV before school.
2. Can you _____ Paola to buy some milk?
3. Just a minute! _____ for me!
4. I _____ you feel better soon.
5. Did you _____ Mr Green on the news last night?
6. Mike can't _____ where he left his phone.

3 ⭐⭐ Circle the correct verbs.

1. Can you **borrow** / **lend** me five euros?
2. My story's **won** / **earned** first prize in a competition!
3. The girl in this advert **reminds** / **remembers** me of you.
4. I never **watch** / **see** TV commercials because I find them really annoying.
5. I **wait** / **hope** Real will win the match.
6. Alfie **spends** / **wastes** hours playing video games. His mum thinks he is **spending** / **wasting** his time.

4 ⭐⭐ Tick (✓) the sentences that are correct. Correct the sentences that are wrong.

1. A lot of food is spent every day. If a food item is going to expire, supermarkets just throw it in the rubbish. ☐
   _____
2. Did you see the photos I posted online? ☐
   _____
3. I wait this T-shirt doesn't shrink when I wash it! ☐
   _____
4. Will you borrow me your pen for a minute? ☐
   _____
5. Celebrities can earn a lot of money by appearing in adverts. ☐
   _____
6. Can you remember me what your name is? ☐
   _____

5 ⭐⭐⭐ Complete the sentences so they are true for you.

1. The best advert I've seen recently is
   _____.
2. I only spend money on something if
   _____.
3. I watch/don't watch adverts on TV because
   _____.
4. One day I hope
   _____.
5. I must remember to
   _____.

Grammar
Reflexive pronouns

1 ⭐ **Choose the correct word for each sentence.**

1. me / myself
   a) The woman asked _____ what my favourite brand of shampoo was.
   b) If you won't buy me some chocolate, I'll buy it _____!
2. you / yourself
   a) Do you find it easy to express _____ in words?
   b) Can I give _____ a free sample of this new drink?
3. her / herself
   a) Did Gabriela write the essay _____?
   b) The teacher never shouts, but everyone respects _____.
4. it / itself
   a) That ad's on all the time and I hate _____!
   b) The dog hasn't really hurt _____ – it's just an advert!
5. us / ourselves
   a) Did you recognize _____ in the video?
   b) We couldn't believe it when we saw _____ on TV!
6. them / themselves
   a) The director told them to relax and be _____.
   b) These crisps are delicious! Have you tried _____?

2 ⭐⭐ **Complete the sentences with reflexive pronouns.**

1. If you burn _____, this cream will really help.
2. My dad's teaching _____ English.
3. Did you and Jack enjoy _____ at Harry Potter World?
4. I think that Angela is old enough to look after _____.
5. Why don't we treat _____ to an ice cream?
6. They made the poster _____.

3 ⭐⭐⭐ **Complete the article with reflexive and object pronouns.**

Schoolboy points out grammar mistake to multinational company

15-year-old Albert Gifford was helping (1) _____ to breakfast one morning when he noticed a mistake on the carton of orange juice in front of (2) _____. After reading that the juice was made from 'the most tastiest' oranges, he wasn't the only one who was surprised. His mum couldn't believe it either when he told (3) _____! The 15-year-old decided to write a letter of complaint to the directors of the supermarket which produces the juice, but got no reply from (4) _____ until his local newspaper reported the story. Finally, the supermarket's management team apologized to Albert, saying that members of their design team should have spotted the mistake (5) _____ and promising to correct (6) _____.

4 ⭐⭐⭐ **Complete the second sentence so that it has a similar meaning to the first. Use the words in brackets and reflexive pronouns.**

1. Do you have an idea what kind of person you are? (know)
   Do you _____?
2. My mum sometimes says things when there's nobody around. (talks)
   My mum sometimes _____.
3. Leo finds it easy to say how he feels. (express)
   Leo finds it easy to _____.
4. Are the cookies homemade? (make)
   Did you and Ben _____?
5. My grandparents need someone to take care of them. (look after)
   My grandparents can't _____.

Home   About   Blog

Why you are wrong if you think you aren't influenced by advertising

1 We like to believe that we make our own decisions about what to buy, wear or eat, but we are all influenced by advertising much more than we know. Modern advertising companies are experts in human psychology, and this means they are very good at getting 'inside our heads' and influencing what we do.

2 Because we constantly see adverts everywhere it's easy to believe they've stopped having any **power** over us. In fact, the opposite is true – as the big brands know very well. If we see the same ad all the time for, for example, a certain brand of soft drink or fast food restaurant, we are likely to eventually buy the drink or go to the restaurant simply because it's become so familiar. Because we've seen it over and over again, we feel we 'know' it in some way and, more importantly, we can trust it. Human beings are social animals and we feel safe when we do what everyone else is doing.

3 Advertisers are also very good at taking advantage of our feelings of **insecurity** – our worries about how we look and how others see us. Ads for brands of clothing and beauty products often work like this. They make us believe that it's possible to **attain** a better version of ourselves … if only we buy a certain product. Adverts for **insurance** companies exploit the 'what if' factor – What if … my phone is stolen, I lose my keys, I miss my flight, etc. The ads make us imagine these things happening and, for a moment, they seem very real!

4 But the best ads work by getting us to make associations and link products with our dreams and desires – how we would like our lives to be. So in an advert for a sports shoe, we see images of successful athletes with happy, **uplifting** music in the background, whereas an ad for jeans shows us cool, good-looking people in exciting places. We don't **consciously** believe that buying the products will make our lives more like the people in the ads, but the positive associations are very powerful. Test this for yourself. Next time you're looking online at an expensive pair of trainers, ask yourself WHY you want them so much more than other, cheaper shoes.

Reading

1 Read and listen to the article and match the paragraphs with the summaries a–d. 25

a We trust a product depending on how often we see it advertised. ___
b The most effective adverts get us to make connections. ___
c Advertisers use our fears and worries to make us buy things. ___
d We don't realize how much advertising affects us. ___

2 Match the words in bold in the text with definitions 1–6.

1 a feeling of not believing in yourself and not having any confidence ___
2 making you feel happy and full of positive feelings ___
3 in a deliberate way ___
4 control or influence over people and things ___
5 to get or achieve something, especially after a lot of effort ___
6 an agreement with a company in which you regularly pay them money and they cover your costs if you have an accident, have something stolen, etc. ___

3 Read the article again. Circle T (true) or F (false). Correct the false sentences.

1 Advertisers use their understanding of how people feel and think to create ads. T F
2 If we see an advert a lot, we have less confidence in the product it is selling. T F
3 Humans don't usually enjoy being the same as other people. T F
4 Advertisements often work by making us believe we can improve ourselves. T F
5 Advertisers try to sell us our own dreams. T F
6 People often decide to buy a product because they're convinced it will change their lives. T F

Listening

LIFELONG LEARNING STRATEGY

Predicting what you are going to hear

Use the questions to predict what you are going to hear. This will make it easier for you to pick out the information you need when you listen.

You are going to listen to an interview with Sindy, who works in advertising. Which of the following do you think she might have to do in her job?

meet people ☐   send emails ☐

dress casually ☐   negotiate with people ☐

give presentations ☐

1 Listen and check your answers to the question above. Did you predict correctly?))) 26

2 Listen again. Complete the sentences about Sindy with a word or phrase.

1 She sells _____ for two separate magazines.
2 She starts work at _____ in the morning.
3 One thing she enjoys about her job is learning about future _____.
4 School and university didn't teach her how to _____ with clients.
5 She advises anyone who wants to work in advertising to _____ in an advertising agency.

3 Circle T (true) or F (false).

1 Dealing with fashion companies is part of her job.   T F
2 She uses the telephone a lot during the day.   T F
3 She only works in the daytime.   T F
4 Her job involves dealing with finances.   T F
5 She completed a marketing degree at university.   T F

Speaking

4 Circle the correct words to complete the presentation. Listen and check.))) 27

Ali: Hello! We're Ali and Sam and we're taking part in a charity fundraising campaign this week. We're raising money for Cancer Research UK – a charity which funds research into cancer. Its aim is to find a cure for cancer.

Sam: Cancer Research UK has saved millions of lives by discovering new ways to prevent, diagnose and treat cancer. Survival rates have significantly improved over the past 40 years. (1) **We're sure you'll** / **You ought to** agree that this is a fantastic cause.

Ali: That's why we're painting fingernails pink this lunchtime. We've done ours already. (2) **Don't** / **Do** they look great? It costs just one pound. You (3) **treat yourself** / **really should** have yours done too!

Sam: We (4) **'re sure** / **guarantee** that all of our profits will go directly to Cancer Research UK. So (5) **don't** / **please**, come to the classroom this lunchtime and show your support!

Writing

5 Complete the sentences with the words in the box.

also   although   but   however
moreover   other

1 On the one hand, teenagers are old enough to think for themselves. On the _____ hand, they may not be aware of the tricks advertisers use.
2 Sometimes I like an advert, _____ then forget what it was for!
3 _____ I hate adverts, I know they influence me.
4 Not only do adverts provide useful information, they can _____ be entertaining.
5 Companies continue to spend a lot of money on advertising. _____, retail sales are decreasing.
6 Advertising shouldn't be allowed in schools. _____, TV adverts aimed at young children should be banned.

Progress check

Vocabulary
Advertising

1 Complete the sentences with the words in the box.

> advertising campaign   celebrity
> consumer   eye-catching   go viral
> hype   jingles   online ads
> peer pressure   persuasive

1 Supermarket advertising uses _____ images of food and drink to attract the customer.
2 _____ are tunes that are designed to stay in your head.
3 The aim of advertising is to convince the _____ that he or she can't live without the product.
4 Some adverts try to be _____ by telling us that we're getting a bargain.
5 When a(n) _____ tells us he or she uses a product, it makes it seem glamorous.
6 Sometimes the _____ about a product makes the customer expect too much from it!
7 Videos _____ when millions of people watch them online within a few days.
8 _____ makes us feel that a product is essential if we want to be part of the 'in-crowd'.
9 Some multinational companies are willing to spend millions of dollars on a(n) _____.
10 Many of the _____ that appear on your computer screen have been specially selected to appeal to you.

Easily confused verbs

2 Circle the correct words.

1 I never **spend / waste** money on things I don't need.
2 Can you **remember / remind** what that funny advert was for?
3 The magician told us to **see / watch** him carefully.
4 I can't **hope / wait** to see the photos!
5 Owen didn't expect his film to **earn / win** an award.
6 Don't **borrow / lend** my phone without asking me!

Grammar
Relative pronouns

3 Join the sentences using relative pronouns.

1 Advertising gives information about a product. This information isn't always true.
_____
2 Amazon is an online store. You can buy many different products there.
_____
3 In 1998 two American students set up a company. Its name was Google.
_____
4 Teenagers are consumers. They get most of their information through digital media.
_____

Indefinite pronouns

4 Complete the second sentence so that it has a similar meaning to the first. Use the words in the box.

> anyone   anything   anywhere
> something   somewhere

1 I only buy things that I need.
   I never buy _____.
2 We want to ask you a question. We want to ask you _____.
3 I wonder why no one liked the advert.
   Why didn't _____?
4 Suzy wants to visit a place she's never been before.
   Suzy wants to visit _____.
5 I've looked everywhere, but I still haven't found my socks!
   I can't _____!

Reflexive pronouns

5 Circle the correct words.

1 Have you ever asked **yourself / myself** what the world would be like without advertising?
2 When Penny's too tired to cook, she often treats **herself / itself** to a takeaway pizza.
3 Carrie and I took this great picture of **themselves / ourselves** on her phone.
4 Can you and Daniel walk home by **yourself / yourselves**?

70

Extension

Cumulative vocabulary

1 Complete the sentences with a word from box A and a word from box B.

> **A**
> ~~crowd-funding~~ eye-catching 50%
> peer target
>
> **B**
> adverts audience ~~campaign~~
> discount pressure

The parents started an online _crowd-funding_ _campaign_ to raise enough money to finish building the school.

1 Teens who are interested in fashion are the _____ _____ for this TV show.
2 These _____ _____ use bright colours and attractive photographs to attract a wider audience.
3 Normally these trainers cost more than 100 euros but I got a _____ _____.
4 Some teenagers do certain things because of _____ _____. They want to be accepted by their classmates.

2 Complete the second sentence so that it has a similar meaning to the first. Use the words in the box.

> go viral   raise money   treat yourself

1 You should be nice to yourself and allow yourself to buy some designer jeans.
   You should _____.
2 The charity is trying to get the cash to help the victims of the hurricane.
   The charity is trying to _____.
3 After the funny ad spread all over the internet, they began selling twice as many products.
   Sales of the product doubled after the ad _____.

More practice
> Grammar reference p98
> Advance your vocabulary p110
> Writing hub p126
> Phrase book pp148–149
> Wordlist pp151–157

Cumulative grammar

3 Circle the correct words.

The art of rhetoric

What is it?

Rhetoric is the art of (1) **persuading / to persuade** people through effective speaking and writing.

*Who (2) **did invent / invented** it?*

The Ancient Greeks in 600 BC. In those days, the art of rhetoric (3) **considered / was considered** an important skill which every educated person (4) **must / had to** learn.

(5) **Do most people learn / Are most people learning** this skill nowadays?

No. It (6) **used to be / was being** an important part of education, but since the early 20th century, many schools and universities (7) **stopped / have stopped** teaching it.

Why is it so important?

If you (8) **learn / 'll learn** the art of rhetoric, you'll be able to persuade and influence other people more effectively. It will also (9) **help / be helping** you judge whether other people's arguments make sense or not. Think how useful this skill (10) **has to / might** be when you're trying to convince your parents to let you do (11) **anything / something** that they don't want you to do!

What's the connection between rhetoric and advertising?

Many of the persuasive techniques (12) **who / which** ad agencies use are based on the rules of rhetoric. When we allow (13) **ourselves / us** to be influenced by them, we give another person control over our minds. Studying rhetoric allows you to see when someone is (14) **saying / telling** you lies and to make your own decisions about what you want to buy.

UNIT 9 GET READY FOR YOUR EXAMS!

Vocabulary review

Revision

1 Match words 1–6 with categories a–f.

1 education
2 often
3 pass
4 said
5 extremely
6 carried out

a) a reporting verb
b) a phrasal verb
c) an adverb of degree
d) an adverb of frequency
e) a noun
f) a verb which collocates with 'exams'

2 Complete the text with the words in exercise 1.

Taking an exam or test – and not being able to answer the questions – is a(n) (1) _____ common bad dream – and not only for school children and students. Lots of adults who haven't taken an exam for years have the same nightmare. Research that has been (2) _____ into the psychological meaning of dreams has discovered that dreaming about exams is (3) _____ connected to general feelings of not being 'good enough' and worrying about how other people see us. The pressure to (4) _____ exams and succeed in (5) _____ is connected with stress and anxiety. Rafael Garcia Ramos, a specialist in sleep problems, (6) _____ that people who have these dreams a lot would probably benefit from a general stress treatment or stress reduction.

Reporting verbs

3 Match the reporting verbs in the box with what the people say.

ask   complain   offer   promise   suggest

1 'If you like, I'll test you on important dates in European history.' _____
2 'It's a lovely day! Let's take our books to the park to study!' _____
3 'My brain's exhausted! I can't remember any more facts!' _____
4 'Can I borrow your pen, Liam?' _____
5 'Don't worry, I'll give it back to you!' _____

Phrasal verbs

4 Circle the correct prepositions.

1 I fell **out** / **off** with my friend after she copied my answers in a test!
2 I got **up** / **on** late and was late for the exam.
3 The teacher told us **down** / **off** for making too much noise.
4 My parents say I should spend less time hanging **up** / **out** with my friends!
5 Turn **off** / **after** that music! I can't concentrate!

Adjectives and adverbs

5 Write the words in the correct columns. Some can go in both.

absolutely   early   hard   late
quickly   quite   strange

adjectives	adverbs

6 Complete the conversation with the words in exercise 5.

Teacher: Why did you arrive (1) _____ for the exam?
Student: My alarm clock didn't go off! I ran all the way here and I'm (2) _____ exhausted.
Teacher: You look a bit (3) _____! Why are you wearing one red sock and one blue sock?
Student: I had to get dressed really (4) _____. It was (5) _____ difficult to find matching socks.
Teacher: Well, please try (6) _____ to wake up (7) _____ tomorrow!
Student: Yes, Miss, I will.

Easily confused words

7 The words in bold are incorrect. Write the correct words from the box.

hope journey lend remind spend

1 I **wait** I have time to answer all the questions on the exam paper. _____
2 **Remember** me to set my alarm for 6am tomorrow! _____
3 The **trip** to school today took me nearly an hour! _____
4 How long are you going to **waste** revising for the exam? _____
5 Can you **borrow** me your watch for the exam tomorrow? _____

Noun suffixes

8 Match root words 1–6 with suffixes a–f to make nouns.

1 disappear   a) ment
2 personal   b) ion
3 relation   c) ance
4 achieve   d) ness
5 possess   e) ship
6 sad   f) ity

9 Complete the sentences with the correct form of the nouns in exercise 8.

1 Some _____ are more suited to exams than others!
2 You aren't allowed to bring _____ like mobile phones into the exam room.
3 Academic _____ are important, but you can still be successful without them!
4 If you have a good _____ with your teachers, ask them for advice about how to revise.
5 The head teacher expressed her _____ that students at her school had been caught cheating.
6 The police are currently investigating the _____ of some exam papers at a school in Sussex.

10 Circle the correct words.

The LONDON Knowledge

It isn't (1) **easy / easiest / easily** to become a taxi driver if you live in London. In order to drive one of the famous black cabs, you need to know the centre of this (2) **tiny / huge / furious** city very (3) **good / badly / well** indeed.

Anyone who applies for a(n) (4) **interview / job / degree** as a London 'cabbie' has to take a test called 'The Knowledge'. To prepare for it, you have to be able to (5) **remind / remember / memory** the location of 25,000 streets and 20,000 landmarks in the city centre! This (6) **inform / informed / information** can be found in what is called 'The Blue Book' and it takes most people between two and four years to learn it. Many students (7) **trip / voyage / travel** around the city by moped for hours every day in order to memorize the 320 routes they need to know.

Once they've got this (8) **qualify / qualifying / qualification**, taxi drivers have a job which can be (9) **absolutely / very / a bit** fascinating, depending on who gets into the taxi! Many of them (10) **admit / complain / refuse** that there is too much traffic in London, however, and that they don't (11) **take / make / do** enough money!

Grammar review
Revision

1 Match the phrases 1–10 in bold in the text with grammar areas a–j.

When a spider climbed onto my desk during one exam, I screamed and ran out of the room! (1) **If I hadn't finished writing, I would have failed** the exam because I refused to go back into the exam room!

One boy didn't switch his phone off before an exam and when it rang, he actually answered it! 'I can't talk now, (2) **I'm taking an exam,**' he said. He (3) **was told** to leave the exam room immediately.

During one English exam, I had a mental block and (4) **couldn't remember** how to spell the word 'and'! The annoying thing was that I remembered as soon as I came out of the exam!

(5) **I've never forgotten** what happened in my Grade 5 piano exam. Before I started playing, the examiner said, 'Don't worry if I close my eyes. (6) **I'll be listening.**' Then he closed his eyes and went to sleep! I carried on playing anyway.

I was taking my final exams at school and the room was silent apart from the sound of the supervisor's squeaky shoes as he walked up and down. I knew that (7) **if the noise didn't stop, I wouldn't be able to concentrate** so I asked him to sit down – and he did!

(8) **I'll never forget** my driving test. I was so stressed that when I got to the exam centre, I realized (9) **I'd forgotten** to put my shoes on! I had to take my test wearing my slippers!

(10) **I used to be** very good at Maths, so everyone wanted to sit next to me in Maths tests in order to copy my answers. I solved the problem by writing the wrong answers for people to copy and then rewriting them at the last minute!

a) present continuous ___
b) present perfect ___
c) past perfect ___
d) *used to* ___
e) past passive ___
f) *will / won't* ___
g) future continuous ___
h) modals ___
i) second conditional ___
j) third conditional ___

2 Complete the sentences with the correct form of the words in brackets.

1 I _____ (only just arrive).
2 Hello! _____ (I be late)?
3 If I'm late, I _____ (not be) allowed into the exam room.
4 Tomorrow I _____ (set) an alarm on my phone. I want to be on time!
5 I've forgotten my pen. Please _____ (I borrow) one?
6 I _____ (find) some useful tips while I _____ (revise) for my English exam last night.
7 Marks _____ (give) for using a variety of tenses and other language structures in your answer.

Gerunds and infinitives

3 Complete the exam instructions with the gerund or infinitive form of the verbs in brackets.

* Remember (1) _____ (write) your name clearly at the top of the paper.
* Do not start (2) _____ (look) at the questions until you are told to do so.
* During the exam, (3) _____ (talk) is not allowed. If you need (4) _____ (ask) a question, you should raise your hand.
* Do not look at anyone else's exam paper apart from your own. (5) _____ (cheat) will be punished!
* At the end of the exam, put your pen down when the supervisor tells you to finish (6) _____ (write).

Conditionals

4 Complete the sentences in your own words. Use the first, second or third conditional.

1 If I do well in my exams, _____.
2 If I had gone to bed earlier, _____.
3 If I was on holiday now, _____.
4 I'd go out tonight if _____.
5 The test would have been easy if _____.
6 We'll buy you a tablet if _____.

Reported speech

5 Write what the people say.

1 Phil told me that he had copied my answers.
   _____

2 Tess said that she was going to study all night!
   _____

3 Ellie said that her parents would be disappointed with her marks.
   _____

4 Edward told the teacher that he hadn't finished his essay yet.
   _____

5 Zoe said she couldn't remember anything!
   _____

6 Rewrite the direct speech as reported speech.

1 'I'm not going to do any revision tonight.'
   Amy said _____.
2 'The drama club's making a video next week.'
   Adam said _____.
3 'I have to give first aid to these casualties.'
   The paramedic said_____.
4 'Three great movies came out last year.'
   The journalist said_____.
5 'I'm flying to Berlin tomorrow!'
   Chloe said _____.
6 'I watched a great film yesterday.'
   Sophie said _____.

Verb tenses

7 Complete the text with the correct form of the verbs in brackets.

What is Mensa?

Mensa (1) _____ (be) a society for very clever people! You're only allowed to join Mensa if you (2) _____ (have) a very high IQ – higher than 98% of the population.
Dr Lancelot Ware, from England, and an Australian called Roland Berrill (3) _____ (start) the society in Oxford in 1946. The Second World War (4) _____ (just / finish) when Ware (5) _____ (meet) Berrill on a train and they (6) _____ (start) talking about the subject of intelligence testing. Berrill and Ware, who (7) _____ (study) at Oxford University at the time, had the idea of creating an organization to bring intelligent people together and encourage research into the subject of intelligence.
Since it began, Mensa (8) _____ (attract) members from all over the world who come from many different backgrounds and age groups. Today there (9) _____ (be) about 134,000 'Mensans' in 100 countries.
If you (10) _____ (want) to join Mensa, it's simple. Anyone of any age, background or nationality can apply. You (11) _____ (have) to take an intelligence test first, though!

The passive

8 Complete the second sentence so that it has a similar meaning to the first. Use the active or the passive.

1 Exam papers are often marked by computers.
   Computers _____.
2 How do people measure intelligence?
   How _____.
3 William Shakespeare wrote *Othello*.
   Othello _____.
4 Maybe exams will be banned by the government in the future!
   Maybe _____.

KEEP CALM AND REVISE YOUR ENGLISH!

It's exam time again, but don't panic! When it comes to English exams, all you need is a plan of action and a few basic study techniques to get you through.

1 _____
Don't leave your revision to the last minute! Remember, the goal is to transfer new language from your short-term to your long-term memory. The more often that language is **retrieved** from your memory, the better, which is where language learning apps can help. Some of them are based on a technique called 'spaced repetition' and recycle different words for you to review every so often.

2 _____
Avoid revising for hours and hours without taking a break. Research shows that studying in spells of 20–30 minutes works better because your **concentration** is much higher. It's no good planning to revise 200 words of English vocabulary in one day, for example, because the average person can only remember between 10 and 20 words per study hour.

3 _____
Just looking at lists of vocabulary will not help you **memorize** it! In order to do that, you have to put pen to paper and make new lists or draw 'word maps'. Grouping words together from the same subject area is a good approach because it matches the brain's natural system for **classifying** information. Colourful notes are easier to remember than black and white ones, so use coloured pens to highlight important information!

4 _____
You might be able to write a brilliant essay in two hours, but what if you only have half an hour in the exam? Practise doing old exam papers and time yourself on the different sections. Once you've done this, you'll feel much more confident about **tackling** the exam.

5 _____
You may not have the chance to prepare for a speaking or listening test by chatting to an English speaker, but you can easily hear natural, spoken English any time you want on the internet. There are lots of podcasts of news and current affairs online and you can also find videos about almost anything!

Reading

1 Read the title of the article. Which of the following do you think the article will NOT include?
   a) Techniques for remembering English vocabulary.
   b) Information about different kinds of English exams you can take.
   c) Advice designed to stop you feeling stressed about exams.

2 Read and listen to the text. Match paragraphs 1–5 with headings a–e. 28
   a) Look at past exams
   b) Make notes
   c) Start early
   d) Experience real English
   e) Set realistic goals

3 Read the text again. Find …
   1 a kind of digital technology which could help you learn words. _____
   2 the maximum amount of time you should study continuously for. _____
   3 two online sources of authentic English. _____

4 Match the words in bold in the text with meanings 1–5.
   1 ability to focus _____
   2 learn _____
   3 taking _____
   4 accessed _____
   5 ordering _____

5 Read the article again. Answer the questions. Write full sentences.
   1 Why is it good to revise vocabulary frequently?
   _____
   2 When does the ability to concentrate decrease?
   _____
   3 What shouldn't you do when you're trying to learn vocabulary?
   _____
   4 What problem might you have if you don't practise doing old exam papers?
   _____
   5 What should you do if you want to listen to a radio programme in English?
   _____

Listening

1 Listen to a discussion about exams. Match Speakers 1–3 with places of learning a–c. 🔊 29

1 Ben   a) private school
2 Emma   b) state school
3 Alice   c) university

2 Listen again. Choose the correct answers.

1 What does Ben say about exam revision?
   a) His teachers give him no help with it.
   b) He hasn't been taught the skills to do it.
   c) He doesn't have enough time for it.

2 How did Alice prepare for exams at school?
   a) She learned some techniques from other people.
   b) She came up with her own approach.
   c) She used a method which wasn't very effective.

3 How does Alice recommend revising a subject?
   a) By reading through your lesson notes.
   b) By sticking your lesson notes on the wall.
   c) By creating your own material from your lesson notes.

4 According to Alice, when is the best time to listen to music?
   a) While you're revising.
   b) When you stop revising to have a rest.
   c) When you're relaxing in bed.

3 Circle T (true) or F (false).

1 Ben has just taken his GCSE exams.   T F
2 Emma doesn't get any help with revision at school.   T F
3 Alice has always had problems with exams.   T F
4 Ben likes to have silence when he's revising.   T F

Speaking

4 Read part of a debate. Then complete it with the phrases in the box. Listen and check. 🔊 30

> Another argument is that
> I'm sorry, but I completely disagree
> In my opinion
> That's an interesting point
> That's not really true, is it

Gus: I'd like to begin by saying that I definitely think it's more important to learn Mandarin nowadays. I don't think English will be very useful in the future.

Vicky: (1) _____! English is an international language and everyone needs to speak it.

Gus: It is now, but what about the future? China is becoming an important economic power. (2) _____, more people will soon be learning Mandarin instead of English.

Vicky: (3) _____? Mandarin will never be spoken by more people because it's a much harder language to learn.

Gus: That's not true for everyone. People from other Asian countries might find it easier than English.

Vicky: (4) _____, but I still can't imagine people in Spain learning Mandarin at school instead of English!

Gus: But Mandarin is already being taught in some British schools. (5) _____, it makes more sense to study a language like Mandarin that isn't so popular.

Writing

5 Rewrite each pair of sentences as one sentence using the words and phrases in brackets.

1 Theo hadn't done any revision. However, he passed the test! (although)
   _____

2 Toby has got a strange illness. Therefore he won't be able to take the exam. (due to)
   _____

3 I'm in the school play next week. I've got my violin exam, too! (in addition)
   _____

4 Eleanor is very intelligent. On the other hand, she can be lazy. (but)
   _____

Progress check

Vocabulary

1 Choose the correct answers.

1. The library is a(n) _____ place to study because talking isn't allowed!
   a) exciting   b) lively   c) peaceful
2. Ewan wants to _____ a video blog of himself revising!
   a) take   b) make   c) get
3. My memory is absolutely _____, so I'm really bad at history.
   a) exhausted   b) terrible   c) fascinating
4. It's difficult to _____ the right balance between studying and having fun.
   a) find   b) meet   c) make
5. Will your parents tell you _____ if you fail your driving test?
   a) off   b) up   c) out
6. I always _____ my nails when I'm nervous!
   a) bite   b) cross   c) hold
7. I can't believe how _____ you answered the questions!
   a) quick   b) fast   c) slow
8. Having a nice _____ is just as important as having academic qualifications.
   a) personality   b) identity   c) ethnicity
9. What qualifications do you need to be a make-up _____?
   a) designer   b) artist   c) operator
10. The teacher _____ to let me take the exam because I was 15 minutes late.
    a) complained   b) admitted   c) refused
11. Can you _____ me your geography notes tonight?
    a) borrow   b) lend   c) earn
12. A video of someone falling asleep in an exam has gone _____ on the internet!
    a) viral   b) eye-catching   c) persuasive

Grammar

2 Complete the sentences with the correct form of the verbs in brackets.

1. Are you going _____ (stay) at home and study this weekend?
2. _____ (you / ever write) a long essay in English?
3. Unfortunately, none of the topics I _____ (revise) came up in the exam yesterday.
4. He used _____ (get) bad marks in English tests but recently they _____ (be) much better.
5. Will the exam _____ (mark) by our teacher?
6. What _____ (you do) while I was working in the library?
7. If I _____ (be) you, I'd go to bed early tonight.
8. The teacher asked us if we _____ (feel) ready to take the oral exam.
9. My sister _____ receive) her music exam results yet.
10. The invigilator said that we _____ (get) into trouble if we made any noise.

3 Complete the second sentence so that it has a similar meaning to the first.

1. I didn't read the instructions properly and I wrote my answers in pencil!
   If I _____.
2. My dad graduated from university in 1990.
   1990 was the year _____.
3. I'm sure I've passed the exam because it was really easy!
   I must _____.
4. 'This app can improve your memory,' said the man in the shop.
   The man in the shop said that _____.
5. What can I do to improve my spoken French?
   Is there _____.

78

Extension

Cumulative vocabulary

1 Complete the sentences with the correct form of the words in the box.

> achieve   apply   concentrate
> positive   ~~schedule~~

There's no English test today – it's been _rescheduled_ for next week.

1 To get a grant, you have to complete an online _____ form.
2 You'll lose _____ easily if you haven't had enough sleep.
3 She passed all her exams with top marks – which is a fantastic _____.
4 Learn from your mistakes, think _____ and believe in yourself!

2 Complete the text with the words in the box.

> assess   discovery   incentive
> performance   pressure   purpose
> qualifications   techniques

THE REAL REASON WE NEED EXAMS

When exam time comes round again with all its stress and (1) _____, a lot of students might ask themselves why they are doing this. Is it really necessary to (2) _____ people all the time? Are exams a true test of your ability? It seems unfair to judge someone entirely on their (3) _____ on one day. It's true that there are different (4) _____ you can learn to become more successful at test taking, but should getting good grades be the main (5) _____ to study during the year? Everyone likes to succeed but what, in the end, is this success for? If you have good (6) _____, you can get a good job, but even then you won't be happy unless you are interested in the work for its own sake. And this is the true (7) _____ of education – to find out what you are interested in, good at and want to know more about: in other words self-(8) _____. Exams are there simply to remind us of what we don't know or haven't understood yet.

More practice

- Grammar reference p100
- Advance your vocabulary p111
- Writing hub p128
- Phrase book pp148–149
- Wordlist pp151–157

Cumulative grammar

3 Circle the correct words.

Does music help you study?

(1) **To listen / Listening** to certain kinds of music (2) **may / must** help you to study, but it has to be the right kind of music. You should choose tunes that keep you awake, but which (3) **wouldn't / won't** distract you. According to Dr. Masha Godkin, the sound of music activates both the left and right brain at the same time, which can help improve your memory and increase your capacity to learn. However, songs with lyrics are not a good idea, since part of the brain's attention capacity (4) **uses / is used** when you listen to the sound of the human voice.

If you (5) **'re studying / studied** a foreign language, on the other hand, listening to songs is an effective way (6) **learning / to learn** new vocabulary in the target language because it (7) **is stimulating / stimulates** the memory at a deeper and more permanent level than written text. For example, I (8) **was shopping / shopped** in the supermarket recently when a song (9) **was coming / came** on the loud-speaker system that I (10) **used / was used** to love. I was surprised to find that, even though I (11) **didn't hear / hadn't heard** it for more than ten years, I (12) **had / was** able to remember the lyrics almost perfectly.

The power of music as a memory aid can (13) **be exploited / exploit** for other subjects too. Choose a tune and sing a maths formula to it, for example, or the names of the kings and queens of Spain– or (14) **anything / anyone** else that you need to memorize: the melody (15) **would / will** help the words stay in your head. Another area music can help you with is pronunciation. When you sing in another language, the rhythm of the music helps to guide your voice and makes it (16) **easier / easiest** to produce the words with the correct pronunciation. Learning songs and poems can even help train your ear so that your listening comprehension improves too.

SUMMER STUDY STRATEGIES

Here are the ways I hope to improve my English over the summer:

- [ ] Go to the library and borrow the English language version of a book that I have already read in my own language.
- [ ] Write a summer diary in English about what I have done.
- [ ] Use the internet to talk to and email English-speaking friends in other countries.
- [ ] Listen to English news on the radio or internet.
- [ ] Bake a cake using a recipe in English.
- [ ] Label the photos in my albums with English captions.
- [ ] Go to my local tourist office and get information about my area in English.
- [ ] Test myself on how long I can speak with a friend in English without using a single word of my own language – try to increase the time by two minutes every time. Compete against each other!
- [ ] Write a simple song in English with a friend and record it on my mobile phone.
- [ ] Go on an English-language tour of my local town or city. I will pretend I am a tourist!
- [ ] Use my mobile phone to record my voice speaking in English to improve my pronunciation. I will also interview my friends in English!
- [ ] Try to learn more about my favourite hobby using English websites.
- [ ] Go to a museum and read or listen to the information in English.
- [ ] Create a wiki and put up my favourite quotes and sayings in English. Record them using voice recording apps.

My targets for the summer:

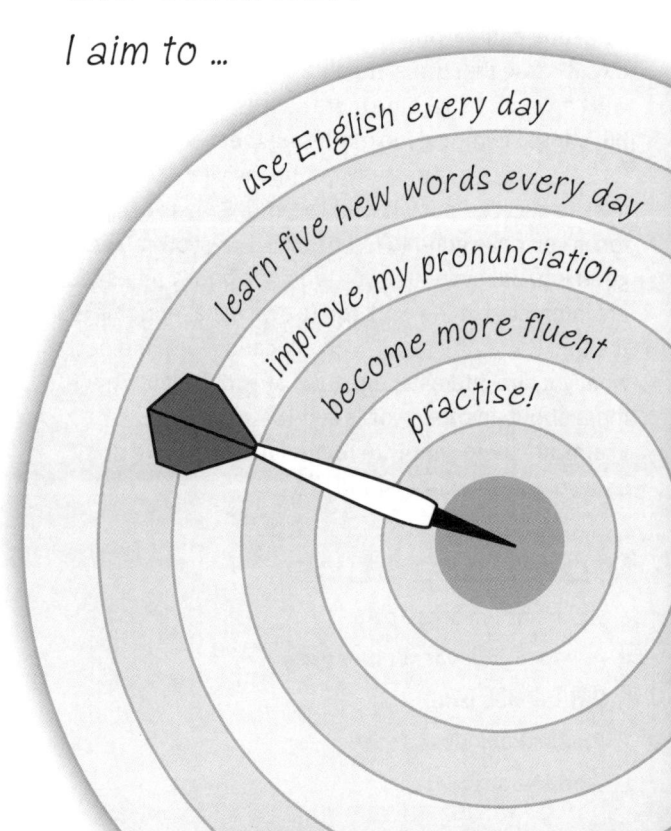

I aim to ...

- use English every day
- learn five new words every day
- improve my pronunciation
- become more fluent
- practise!

SELF-STUDY BANK

Contents

Grammar reference Starter unit–Unit 9	82–101
Advance your vocabulary Starter unit–Unit 9	102–111
Writing hub Units 1–9	112–129
External exam trainer	130–147
Phrase book	148–149
Pronunciation reference	150
Wordlist	151–157
Irregular verbs	158–160

Grammar reference

STARTER

Present simple and present continuous

present simple	present continuous
I **study** English three times a week.	I'**m studying** English at the moment.
He **starts** his job in June.	He **is staying** in Italy now.
We **don't** usually **go** to the beach in summer.	We **aren't lying** on the beach at the moment.
Do you **go** abroad every year?	**Is** the sun **shining** today?
Yes, we **do**. / No, we **don't**.	Yes, it **is**. / No, it **isn't**.

- we use the present simple for habits and routines. We can use it with adverbs of frequency (*never, sometimes, always,* etc) and time expressions (*every day, twice a week*, etc).
- we use the present continuous to describe what is happening at the moment or temporary situations. We can use it with time expressions (*at the moment, now, today*, etc).

Gerunds and infinitives

- We use gerunds:

  a) in place of the subject or object of a sentence
  Running is really good for you.

  b) after certain verbs such as *avoid, dislike, don't mind, enjoy, finish, hate, like, love, recommend, stop*
  I love running!

  c) after prepositions
  He's good at running.

- we form the gerund by adding *-ing* to the infinitive. The spelling rules are the same as for the present continuous.

- We use infinitives

  a) after certain verbs such as *afford, decide, help, hope, need, remember, want*
  I need to read that book before the lesson.

  b) to show reasons for doing things
  We went into town to buy dinner.

  c) after adjectives, eg *easy, happy*, etc
  It's difficult to learn a new language.

Past simple and past continuous

past simple	past continuous
I **studied** French last year.	I **was studying** in Paris.
He **went** to Rome on holiday.	He **was visiting** his aunt.
We **didn't go** to the beach last summer.	We **weren't lying** on the beach.
Did you **visit** an ancient site last month?	**Was** it **raining**?
Yes, we **did**. / No, we **didn't**.	Yes, it **was**. / No, it **wasn't**.

- we use the past simple to talk about completed actions in the past
  I listened to the radio this morning.
- to form the negative and questions, we use the auxiliary verb *do*
- we use the past continuous to describe actions that were in progress in the past
- the form is *was / were* + verb + *-ing*
- we form questions with *was / were* + subject + verb + *-ing*. In short answers we use subject + *was / were* without the verb
- we often use the past continuous and the past simple in the same sentence
- we use the past continuous for actions in progress in the past and the past simple for events which interrupt the action in progress
- we use the past simple after *when* and the past continuous after *while*
  I was walking on the beach when I saw my friend.
  While I was walking on the beach, I saw my friend.

used to

used to
I **used to love** ice cream when I was a child.
He **didn't use to like** walking to school.
Did you **use to use** computers at school?
Yes, we **did**. / No, we **didn't**.

- we use *used to* + infinitive without *to* to talk about past habits and states which no longer exist
  *They **used to** live in London, but now they live in Glasgow.*
- to form the negative we use *didn't* + *use to* + infinitive without *to*
- to form questions we use *did* + *use to* + infinitive without *to*. In short answers we only use *do* without the verb

Grammar exercises

STARTER

Present simple and present continuous

1 Circle the correct words.

We **visit** / **'re visiting** York today.
1 I **don't speak** / **'m not speaking** English now.
2 When I **go** / **am going** on holiday, I **want** / **am wanting** to relax.
3 The sun **doesn't shine** / **isn't shining** today.
4 Helen usually **works** / **is working** in an office.

2 Write questions. Use the present simple or the present continuous.

what / you / do / at the moment / ?
What are you doing at the moment?

1 where / you / usually / go on holiday in summer / ?
　_____
2 you / wear / school uniform / today / your / ?
　_____
3 what languages / you / learn / this year / ?
　_____
4 what time / your mum / usually / go to bed / ?
　_____
5 how often / you / study English / ?
　_____

Gerunds and infinitives

3 Complete the table with the verbs in the box.

~~afford~~　arrange　decide　enjoy　finish
learn　look forward to　remember
spend time　want　would like

verb + gerund	verb + infinitive
	afford

4 Complete the sentences with the gerund or the infinitive form of the verbs in brackets.

1 I can't afford _____ (go) on holiday.
2 My friends often spend time _____ (mend) their mountain bikes.
3 When you've finished _____ (try on) your new shoes, can you help me?
4 I don't want _____ (argue) about it.

Past simple and past continuous

5 Complete the sentences with the correct form of the verbs in brackets. Use the past simple or the past continuous.

Where *were you going* (you / go) when I _*saw*_ (see) you?
1 Yesterday I _____ (visit) some monuments and then I _____ (have) lunch in a famous restaurant.
2 John _____ (swim) in the sea when he _____ (see) a dolphin.
3 While I _____ (lie) on the beach, I _____ (fall) asleep.

used to

6 Complete the text with *used to* and the verbs in brackets.

When I was younger, my family *didn't use to go* (not go) abroad. We (1) _____ (visit) my grandparents in Scotland every summer. We (2) _____ (spend) a lot of time outside. We (3) _____ (have) picnics on the beach, but we (4) _____ (not go) swimming because it was too cold!

7 Complete the second sentence so that it has a similar meaning to the first sentence, using the word given. Do not change the word given. You must use between two and five words, including the word given.

Tim only goes to the gym once a month. **OFTEN**
Tim doesn't often go to the gym.

1 We don't have enough money to go on holiday this year. **AFFORD**
We _____ on holiday this year
2 When we were younger we used to worry less. **USE TO**
We _____ so much when we were younger.
3 Walking to school is OK as long as it isn't raining. **MIND**
As long as it is isn't raining, I _____ to school.
4 He talks to his friends online for a long time every day. **SPEND**
He _____ to his friends online every day.

83

Grammar reference

UNIT 1

Present perfect with *just, yet, already, for* and *since*

present perfect
She's **made** a video blog.
We've **created** a website.
I **haven't checked** my email today.
Have you **received** my text?
Yes, I **have**. / No, I **haven't**.

- We use the present perfect to
  a) express an action which started in the past but continues in the present
  Fiona **has known** Sam for ages. They're friends.
  b) talk about an action in the past that we don't know the exact time of
  I've **been** to the circus.
  c) describe events in the past which have had an effect on the current situation
  They've **learned** to juggle. Now they can perform.

- we use the present perfect + *just* to say that something has happened very recently
  Mark **has just arrived**. He got here a minute ago.

- we use the present perfect + *yet* to talk about things which haven't happened (in the past), but that are due to happen (in the future)
  He **hasn't designed** his website **yet**. He's going to start tomorrow.

- we use the present perfect + *already* to describe things which have been completed before the present
  We've **already baked** the cake.

- we use the present perfect + *for* or *since* to talk about the duration of things

- to ask a question about time we use the phrase *How long ...?*
  How long have you **known** Paul?

- we use *for* to describe a period of time
  We've known Paul **for** five years.

- we use *since* to talk about a starting point in time
  We've known Paul **since** 2010.

Present perfect and past simple

- We use the present perfect for
  a) situations that continue into the present
  You've **had** my CD for two weeks.
  b) actions when we don't know the specific time
  I've **walked** on a tightrope.
  c) questions about the past which aren't time specific
  Have you ever **watched** the sun rise?

- we use non-specific time expressions with the present perfect, such as *in the last year, never, recently*. We also use *already, for, just, since, yet*.
  I've **never baked** a cake.
  We've **already started** the course.

- We use the past simple for
  a) completed actions in the past at exact times
  We **went** to the cinema yesterday.
  b) questions about the past with exact timings
  Did you **watch** the sun rise yesterday?

- we use phrases that describe an exact time with the past simple, such as *a week ago, last week, yesterday*
  I **rode** my bike on **Monday**.
  Tim **wrote** that poem **three days ago**.

Grammar exercises

Present perfect with *just, yet, already, for* and *since*

1 Complete the sentences with the present perfect form of the verbs in the box.

> juggle   live   not make

1 My grandad _____ near the beach for years.
2 We _____ with three balls.
3 He _____ any new friends since he changed schools.

2 Write answers using the present perfect. Use *just* and the words in brackets.

> Why are they laughing? (Rob / tell a joke)
> *Because Rob's just told a joke.*

1 Why does Tim look pale? (he / go on a big roller coaster)
_____
2 Why are they happy? (they / perform on stage)
_____
3 Why are you tired? (I / ride a long way on a unicycle)
_____

3 Write sentences with the word in brackets.

> I've done this exercise. (already)
> *I've already done this exercise.*

1 I've bought Sue's birthday present. (already)
_____
2 It's 1pm and you haven't made a video blog. (yet)
_____
3 Has Sarah learned to write code? (yet)
_____

4 Complete the table with the time expressions in the box.

> 10th March   2005   a very long time
> five years   nine o'clock
> several days   six hours   two weeks
> we performed on stage   yesterday

for	since

5 Write questions with *How long …?*

> the juggler / work / in the circus / ?
> *How long has the juggler worked in the circus?*

1 you / study / English / ?
_____
2 she / be / your English teacher / ?
_____
3 they / live / in France / ?
_____
4 he / have / his guitar / ?
_____

Present perfect and past simple

6 Complete the second sentence so that it has a similar meaning to the first sentence, using the word given. Do not change the word given. You must use between two and five words, including the word given.

> Sara went home about five minutes ago. **JUST**
> *Sara's just gone home.*

1 He's still asleep. **YET**
   He hasn't _____.
2 I'm 16 now and I moved to this town when I was 12. **FOR**
   I have _____ four years.
3 She loved dancing when she was a child and she still loves it now. **SINCE**
   She _____ she was a child.
4 The children are still eating their breakfast. **FINISH**
   The children _____ yet.
5 I've met that girl before. **ALREADY**
   I've _____.

7 Circle the correct words.

1 Mel **has performed** / **performed** on stage last week.
2 They **haven't walked** / **didn't walk** on a tightrope since last year.
3 Sally **has learned** / **learned** to ride a unicycle ten years ago.
4 I **haven't read** / **didn't read** that book yet.

Grammar reference

Unit 2

Past perfect and past simple

past perfect	past simple
He'd put out the fire	by the time the firefighters arrived.
He hadn't put out the fire	before the firefighters arrived.
Had he put out the fire	before the firefighters arrived?

- we can use the past perfect and past simple in the same sentence
- we use the past perfect for actions that happened at a time in the past before the main event, which is usually expressed in the past simple.
We'd learned first aid before the accident happened.
I'd helped the survivors by the time the ambulance arrived.
- to form the present perfect affirmative and questions we use had + past participle
- to form the present perfect negative we use hadn't + past participle
- in short answers we only use had / hadn't, without the verb
Had they sent help?
Yes, they had. / No, they hadn't.
- we use time expressions such as after, already, before, by the time and yet with the past perfect
- usually we use time expressions in sentences with both the past simple and the past perfect
She had put on a lifejacket before the boat capsized.
The rescue ship arrived after our ship had sunk.
We were worried, but the captain hadn't given the order to abandon ship yet.
- already goes between had and the past participle
Someone had already called the emergency services, so I didn't have to phone.
- by the time / often goes at the beginning of the sentence and there is a comma before the second clause
By the time I got on deck, the fire had destroyed half the ship.
- by the time can also go in the middle of the sentence. Then we don't use a comma.
The fire had destroyed half the ship by the time I got on deck.

Subject and object questions

- question words can either be the subject or the object of a sentence
- we form subject questions using subject + verb
What happened?
- we form object questions using object + auxiliary verb + subject + verb
What did you do?
- when the question word is the subject of the sentence, we don't use an auxiliary verb
Who supported the anti-bullying campaign?
Many young people supported it.
- when the question is the object of the sentence, we must use an auxiliary verb
Who did they give the money to?
They gave it to **the disaster survivors**.
Where do you live?
I live in **London**.

Grammar exercises

UNIT 2

Past perfect and past simple

1 Circle the correct words.

1 The survivors had been in the water for hours when the rescue workers **found** / **had found** them.
2 I **didn't hear** / **hadn't heard** about the accident before I saw it on the news.
3 The rescue workers had left before we **arrived** / **had arrived**.
4 **Did the victims receive** / **Had the victims received** compensation when you spoke to them?
5 What did you do when the paramedics **arrived** / **had arrived**?
6 We **sent** / **had sent** aid the year before this disaster happened.

2 Complete the sentences with the past perfect form of the verbs in brackets.

1 She didn't know how to give first aid because she _____ (not do) the course yet.
2 After the ship caught fire, we had to jump into the water because they _____ (not put) the lifeboats in the water yet.
3 Before I worked on that cruise ship, I _____ (never travel) by ship.
4 The captain _____ (not call) the emergency services yet.
5 The search and rescue workers _____ (look) in the area before, but then they decided to look again.
6 I read about the accident in the paper after I _____ (hear) about it on the radio.

3 Complete the dialogue with the correct form of the verbs in brackets.

A: What's the matter?
B: My brother (1) _____ (have) an accident yesterday. He (2) _____ (text) me from the hospital to tell me. I went to the hospital, but when I got there he (3) _____ (leave)!
A: Why?
B: I (4) _____ (leave) a message on his phone to tell him I'd come and collect him, but he (5) _____ (not listen) to the message before I (6) _____ (arrive).
A: So he (7) _____ (not know) that you were coming!
B: No!

4 Circle the correct words.

1 The party had started **before** / **after** we arrived.
2 I celebrated with my friends **before** / **after** I'd won the prize.
3 By the time she was 20, she'd **already** / **before** finished university.
4 We ran to the square, but **by the time** / **after** we got there, Sue had left.

Subject and object questions

5 Match the questions 1–6 with the answers a–f.

1 Who does the Red Cross help? ___
2 Who set up the Red Cross? ___
3 What happened in 1859? ___
4 What did Dunant see in Italy? ___
5 Who suffered after the battle? ___
6 Who did Dunant decide to help when he returned home? ___

a) Thousands of wounded soldiers suffered.
b) Jean-Henry Dunant set it up.
c) He saw a terrible battle.
d) He decided to help people who were injured in wars.
e) It helps the victims of war.
f) Dunant travelled to Italy to meet Napoleon.

6 Complete the second sentence so that it has a similar meaning to the first sentence, using the word given. Do not change the word given. You must use between two and five words, including the word given.

We didn't know if any of the passengers were still alive after the accident. **SURVIVED**
<u>We didn't know if anyone had survived the accident.</u>

1 He was very tired in class because he couldn't sleep the night before. **EXHAUSTED**
He hadn't been able to sleep the night before so _____.
2 Which of those people suffered in the earthquake? **VICTIMS**
Who _____?
3 The lifeguards saved him when his boat crashed and sunk. **CAPSIZED**
He was saved by the lifeguards after _____.

87

Grammar reference

Future tenses

will / won't
You**'ll feel** better if you relax.
She **won't go** to university if she fails her exams.
Will your parents **buy** you a car?
Yes, they **will**. / No, they **won't**.

- we use *will* to make predictions about the future
  *I think Dan **will** pass his exams. He's studied hard.*
- we can also use *will* to talk about spontaneous decisions (decisions we make at the time of speaking), offers and promises
  *'Are you going to phone Jane now?' 'No, I'**ll phone** her tomorrow.'*
  *'I don't understand my homework.' 'I'**ll help** you.'*
  *'Can I borrow your tablet? I'**ll be** very careful with it, I promise.'*
- the form is *will / won't* + the infinitive without *to*. In short answers we use *will / won't* without the verb.

be going to
I**'m going to** go on an exchange – it's all organized.
You**'re going to** go to university with those grades.
Maria **is going to** buy a new car. She's already chosen the one she wants.
He **isn't going to** go on holiday this year – he's saving up to buy a house.
Is he **going to** earn enough money?
Yes, he **is**. / No, he **isn't**.

- we use *be going to* to talk about plans or intentions
  *I'**m going to** get a holiday job.*
- the form is *be + (not) going to* + the infinitive without *to*. In short answers we use *be* without the verb.

might
I **might** visit my sister at the weekend.
She **might** be busy.
He **might not** have enough money for a new car.
We **might not** move house until next year.

- we use *might* to talk about possibility in the future, when things aren't certain
  *We're going to go backpacking. We **might** go to Italy, we're not sure yet.*
- the form is *might (not)* + the infinitive without *to*
- we don't usually use *might* in questions

present simple
The course **starts** at 9am.
The train **doesn't depart** until 11.06.
Does the next bus to Liverpool **leave** soon?
Yes, it **does**. / No, it **doesn't**.

- we use the present simple to talk about schedules and timetables in the future
  *Sam's plane **arrives** at 4pm tomorrow.*

present continuous
We**'re visiting** my aunt tomorrow.
They **aren't doing** an English course next summer.
Is he **leaving** tomorrow?
Yes, he **is**. / No, he **isn't**.

- we use the present continuous to talk about arrangements that have been made for the future
  *I'**m starting** my new summer job next week.*

Future continuous

future continuous
I **will be working** in a shop next summer.
Jess **will be arriving** tomorrow afternoon.
I **won't be living** at home next year.
We **won't be studying** at midnight tonight.
What **will** you **be doing** at this time next week?
Will Tom **be studying** at ten o'clock tonight?
Yes, he **will**. / No, he **won't**.

- we use the future continuous to talk about activities that will be in progress at a specific time in the future
  *They **will be doing** the exam at ten o'clock tomorrow morning.*
- we form the future continuous using *will / won't + be +* verb *+ -ing*. In short answers we use *will / won't* without the verb.

Grammar exercises

UNIT 3

Future tenses

1 Match sentences 1–6 with the uses a–f.

1 I'm meeting Joe at 7pm. __
2 He's going to study maths at university. __
3 In 2030, we'll live on the moon. __
4 I'm bored. I'll phone a friend. __
5 The course starts next month. __
6 We might go to India next year. __

a) a prediction about the future
b) a spontaneous decision about the future
c) a future plan
d) a future possibility
e) a future arrangement
f) a future timetable

2 Choose the correct answers.

   A: The phone is ringing.
   B: OK. __ it.
   a) I'll answer   b) I'm going to answer
   c) I might answer

1 A: What are your plans for the summer?
   B: I don't know. __ a course, but I'm not sure.
   a) I'll do   b) I'm going to do
   c) I might do

2 A: What are you doing in the summer?
   B: __ go backpacking for a month. I'm looking forward to it!
   a) We'll   b) We're going to
   c) We might

3 A: Can I borrow your tablet?
   B: OK, but please look after it.
   A: __ be very careful.
   a) I'll   b) I'm going to
   c) I might

3 Write sentences. Use the present simple or the present continuous.

1 Simon's train / arrive / at 12.40 / tomorrow
_____
2 Paula / meet / Simon / at the station
_____
3 then / they / have lunch / with us
_____
4 in the evening / we / go / to a concert
_____
5 the concert / start / at 7.30pm
_____

4 Circle the correct words.

1 We're **going to have** / 'll have a party tonight.
2 I've got a headache. I think **I'll lie down** / 'm lying down.
3 Let's go to the job office. They'll give / 're giving a talk about voluntary work.
4 In the future, I think more people **will study** / are studying abroad.
5 The exam **is starting** / **starts** at 9am tomorrow.

5 Complete the sentences with the correct future form of the verbs in brackets.

1 Don't worry, Jason! I _____ (help) you with your algebra homework.
2 When we're in Paris, we _____ (go up) the Eiffel Tower.
3 I'm busy later. I _____ (go) for a job interview.
4 I'm not sure, but I think it _____ (rain) at the weekend.

Future continuous

6 Complete the sentences with the future continuous form of the verbs in brackets.

1 Liam _____ (not go) backpacking this summer, he _____ (study) in France.
2 At 10am tomorrow morning, I _____ (take) my driving test.
3 This time next week, we _____ (fly) to Mexico. We _____ (not work)!
4 On Monday, Sarah _____ (have) her job interview, she _____ (not relax) at home.

7 Complete questions using the future continuous. Then answer the questions. Use full sentences.

   What _will you be doing_ (you / do) at 4am tomorrow morning?
   I'll be sleeping at 4am tomorrow morning.

1 _____ (you / live) at home this time next year?
_____
2 _____ (you / work) in ten years' time?
_____
3 _____ (you / meet) your friends on Friday night?
_____

Grammar reference

The zero, first, second and third conditional

- conditional sentences have a situation (with an *if* clause) and a consequence. The order of the situation and the consequence is unimportant; the meaning is the same
- we use a comma if the situation comes first
- we don't use a comma if the consequence comes first

zero conditional	
situation	consequence
If it **is** sunny,	he **walks** to school
consequence	situation
We **don't go** to school,	if we **are** sick

- we use the zero conditional to talk about facts or things that are generally true
- we form the zero conditional with *if* + subject + present simple (for the situation) and subject + present simple (for the consequence)

first conditional	
situation	consequence
If they **follow** the rules,	they **won't have** any problems.
consequence	situation
They**'ll be** in trouble	if they **don't get** home on time

- we use the first conditional to talk about possible or probable situations and their consequences in the future
- we form the first conditional with *if* + subject + present simple (for the situation) and subject + *will* / *won't* + infinitive without *to* (for the consequence)
- we can use *unless* instead of *if* in first conditional sentences. *Unless* + affirmative verb = *if* + negative verb
  If we **don't leave** now, we'll be late.
  Unless we **leave** now, we'll be late.

second conditional	
situation	consequence
If we **had** more time,	I **would tell** you all my news.
consequence	situation
They **would split** up	if they **didn't get** on.

- we use the second conditional to talk about hypothetical or unlikely situations and their consequences in the future
  They **wouldn't go** out together if **they didn't get** on.
  (= they do get on so they do go out together)

- we form the second conditional with *if* + subject + past simple (for the situation) and subject + *would* / *wouldn't* + infinitive without *to* (for the consequence)

third conditional	
situation	consequence
If they **had settled** down,	they **would have been** happier.
consequence	situation
We **wouldn't have met**	if we **hadn't taken part** in the show.

- we use the third conditional to imagine the consequences of past situations
- we form the third conditional with *if* + subject + past perfect (for the situation) and subject + *would* / *wouldn't* + *have* + past participle (for the consequence)
  If you **had told** me about the problem, I **would have helped** you.
  (= you didn't tell me, so I didn't help you)
- we can use the short forms of the verbs for both parts of the sentence
  If they **had** already seen the film, they **would** have said.
  If they**'d** already seen the film, they**'d** have said.

Adverbs of possibility and probability

- we can use *maybe*, *perhaps*, *definitely* and *probably* to talk about possibility and probability
- *Maybe* and *perhaps* go at the beginning of a sentence or clause
  Maybe the world would be a better place if everyone listened more actively.
  After learning about active listening, **perhaps** they will try the techniques.
- *Definitely* and *probably* go after affirmative auxiliary verbs (*will*, *would*, etc) and forms of *be*
  If I were you, I**'d definitely** talk to Sam about the problem.
  We**'re probably** going to learn more about communication.
- *Definitely* and *probably* go before negative auxiliary verbs (*won't*, *wouldn't*, *shouldn't*, etc) and forms of *be*
  We **definitely aren't** going to learn if we don't listen carefully.
  There **probably wouldn't** be any wars if people really listened to each other.

Grammar exercises

The zero, first, second and third conditional

1 Write first conditional sentences.

if / I / go / abroad / I / make / new friends
If I go abroad, I'll make new friends.

1 if / I / see Jackie / I / give / her / your message
_____

2 we / be / tired / tomorrow / if / not go / to bed / soon
_____

3 if / you / not listen / you / not understand
_____

2 Correct the second conditional sentences.

We'd save a lot of water if we don't have a shower every day. ✗
*We'd save a lot of water if we **didn't** have a shower every day.*

1 If he doesn't frown so often, people would like him more. ✗
_____

2 I would work in a shop if I won't be so shy. ✗
_____

3 If I'd see a job advertisement for the perfect job, I'd apply for it. ✗
_____

3 Complete the first and second conditional sentences with the correct form of the verbs in brackets.

1 If I _____ (get) good marks in the exams, my parents will buy me a new bike.

2 We'll go to the beach if it _____ (be) hot tomorrow.

3 I'd phone my mum if I _____ (get) lost in a big city.

4 I _____ (go) to the cinema if it rains tomorrow.

4 Match the sentence beginnings with the endings.

1 If he had listened in class, —
2 If I had studied more, —
3 He wouldn't have fallen out with Jake —
4 You'd have met my cousins —

a) if he had taken his advice.
b) he would have understood the exercise.
c) if you'd come to the cinema with us.
d) I'd have got a higher mark.

5 Rewrite the sentences in the third conditional.

He didn't run so he missed the train.
If he'd run, he wouldn't have missed the train.

1 She didn't fill in the application form correctly so she didn't get the job.
_____

2 They didn't see the concert because they didn't buy tickets.
_____

3 I didn't have my mobile so I didn't phone you.
_____

Adverbs of possibility and probability

6 Rewrite the sentences with the adverbs in brackets in the correct place.

You shouldn't hold hands in public. (maybe)
Maybe you shouldn't hold hands in public.

1 You should shake hands. (perhaps)
_____

2 In Japan you shouldn't kiss people you don't know on the cheek. (probably)
_____

3 If I were you, I wouldn't shout. (definitely)
_____

7 Complete the second sentence so that it has a similar meaning to the first sentence, using the word given. Do not change the word given. You must use between two and five words, including the word given.

It's not a good idea to do that. **WERE**
If I were you, I wouldn't do that.

1 I'm sure you'll get on with my cousin if you meet her. **DEFINITELY**
If you meet my cousin, _____ with her.

2 He hopes we never have an argument – that would upset him a lot. **FELL OUT**
He would be very upset _____.

3 The reason she was so angry is that you didn't remember her name. **WOULDN'T**
If you hadn't forgotten her name, _____ so angry.

Grammar reference

The passive

present simple passive
- + Science competitions **are held** every year.
- - Projects from abroad **aren't accepted**.
- ? When **is** the winner **announced**?

past simple passive
- + The machine **was designed** by Edison.
- - Batteries **weren't used** for power.
- ? When **was** it **invented**?

future passive: will
- + Cars **will be driven** by remote control.
- - Roads **won't be used** so often.
- ? **Will** pollution **be reduced** in the future?

- we use the passive:
  a) to emphasize the action of the sentence
  b) when we don't know for sure who does the action
  c) to describe something which is happening directly to the subject of the sentence
  d) to describe a series of processes
  e) more in writing than in speaking

- we form the present simple passive using the present tense of *be* + past participle of the verb
  New discoveries **are made** *every year.*

- if we use adverbs of frequency, they go between *be* and the past participle
  Girls **aren't often encouraged** *to study science.*

- we form the past simple passive using the past tense of *be* + past participle of the verb
  The radio **was invented** *in the 19th century.*
  We **weren't asked** *to do a science project.*

- we form the future passive using *will / won't* + *be* + past participle of the verb
  I hope a cure **will be discovered** *soon.*
  The prizes **won't be given** *to the winners until next week.*

- to make questions in the present simple passive and the past simple passive we use (question word) + *be* + subject + past participle
  How **are** *the experiments* **designed**?
  Was *the first robot* **invented** *many years ago?*

- we use *by* in passive sentences if we want to express who or what does the action
  Planes were invented **by** *the Wright brothers.*
  The prize was awarded **by** *the judges.*

Active and passive voice

active	A celebrity **presented** the prizes.
passive	The prizes **were presented by** a celebrity.

- in active sentences, the subject is the person or thing that does the action
  Hassan *invented a new app.*

- in passive sentences, the subject is the person or thing that receives the action of the verb
  A new app *was invented by Hassan.*

- we also use the passive when we do not know who does the action
  active: People **produce** *new apps all the time.*
  passive: New apps **are produced** *all the time.*

- we use the passive in written English more than in spoken English

- we often use the passive in writing to describe a process
  First a prototype **is produced** *and then it is* **tested**.

- we use *by* in passive sentences if we want to express who or what does an action
  The Kodak camera was produced **by** *George Eastman.*

Grammar exercises

The passive

1 Write sentences in the present simple passive.

1 the science fair / hold / every four years
   _____
2 students / not allow / in the laboratory without a teacher
   _____
3 animals / not use / in the experiments
   _____
4 new discoveries / write about / in magazines
   _____
5 new research / do / every year
   _____

2 Complete the sentences with the past simple passive form of the verbs in brackets.

1 My camera _____ (steal) from my bag.
2 Bottles _____ (not recycle) 30 years ago.
3 My mum _____ (give) a promotion last week.
4 Text messages _____ (not send) 20 years ago.
5 The best projects _____ (design) by two teenagers.
6 The competition _____ (not televise).

3 Write sentences in the future passive.

1 pollution / will / reduce / by the government
   _____
2 the prize / will / win / by the French students
   _____
3 our car / will not / repair / until next week
   _____
4 many shoplifters / will / never / catch
   _____
5 our team / will not / beat / in this competition
   _____

4 Complete the sentences with *was*, *is* or *will be*.

1 English _____ spoken all over the world.
2 The town centre _____ closed next week.
3 A suspect _____ arrested last night.
4 He _____ questioned by the police tomorrow morning.
5 The 2010 World Cup _____ won by Spain.

5 Correct the sentences.

1 The 2028 Olympics will hold in Los Angeles. ✗
   _____
2 London visits millions of tourists every year. ✗
   _____
3 Your application form didn't fill in correctly. ✗
   _____
4 Be careful! That bottle make of glass. ✗
   _____

6 Write passive questions for these answers.

Where _____*is gold found*_____ ?
Gold is found in South Africa.
1 When _____?
   The telephone was invented in 1876.
2 What _____?
   Her ring is made of gold.
3 Where _____?
   The airplane was invented in France.
4 When _____?
   A cure for most diseases will be discovered soon.

Active and passive voice

7 Complete the second sentence so that it has a similar meaning to the first sentence, using the word given. Do not change the word given. You must use between two and five words, including the word given.

I left my bag on the beach while I was swimming and someone took it. **STOLEN**
My *bag was stolen* from the beach while I was swimming.

1 Which city will host the science fair next year? **HELD**
   In which city will the science fair _____ next year?
2 The police came and took the man away. **ARRESTED**
   The man _____ the police.
3 Unfortunately, there's no more milk in the shop today. **SOLD**
   Unfortunately, all the milk _____ today.
4 The cleaners had put the papers in the rubbish before class. **THROWN**
   The papers _____ in the rubbish before class by the cleaners.

Grammar reference

Unit 6

Modals of ability and possibility, obligation and prohibition

present	past
ability and possibility	
+ You **can** open a bank account when you're a child.	+ I **could** get a credit card when I was 18.
- You **can't** take out a bank loan until you're 18.	- I **couldn't** use a social networking site when I was 12.
obligation and prohibition	
+ You **must** / **have to** be careful online.	+ Kate **had to** go to the police when her identity card was stolen.
- You **mustn't** give your personal details online.	
no obligation	
- I **don't have to** change my password – it's safe.	- They **didn't have to** pay back the stolen money.

- we use *can* and *can't* to talk about ability and possibility in the present
  *John **can** log onto the site, but he **can't** change his password – he's forgotten how to do it.*
  *Where **can** I buy some stamps?*

- we use *could* and *couldn't* to talk about ability and possibility in the past
  *The police **couldn't** find the criminals.*
  *The fraudster **could** design websites that looked authentic.*

- we use *must*, *mustn't* and *have to* to talk about obligation and prohibition in the present
  *You **mustn't** put letters from the bank in the bin. You **have to** shred them first.*
  *You **must** protect yourself from online fraud.*

- we use *had to* to talk about obligation in the past. There is no past form for *must*.
  *I **had to** change my password after my account was hacked.*

- we use *don't have to* when there is no obligation in the present. This means 'it is not necessary'.
  *I **don't have to** do my homework tonight. I can do it tomorrow.*

- we use *didn't have to* when there is no obligation in the past
  *They **didn't have to** go to prison – they had to do community service instead.*

Modals of deduction

certainty
They **must** be away, the car isn't there.
(= I am sure this is true)
They **can't** be in Greece, they don't like hot weather!
(= I am certain this is not true)

possibility
They **could** / **might** be in Scotland, they often go there.
(= I think this is possible, but I'm not sure)
They **might not** phone us.
(= I'm not sure if it's possible or not)

- we use *must*, *could* / *might* (*not*) and *can't* to express (deduce) the probability of a situation

- we use *must* to talk about something that is certain or logical
  *Her shoes are wet, it **must** be raining.*

- we use *might* (*not*) and *could* to talk about something that is possible but not certain
  *Mario **might** be Spanish or he **could** be Italian; I'm not sure.*

- we use *can't* to talk about something that is impossible
  *He **can't** be the thief – he was away on holiday when the crime happened.*

Grammar exercises

Modals of ability and possibility, obligation and prohibition

1 Circle the correct words.

1. We **mustn't** / **don't have to** wear a uniform at our school.
2. Sara **has to** / **can** cycle to school because there isn't a bus.
3. They **have to** / **can** leave by 6pm or they'll miss the train.
4. I **mustn't** / **can't** read your writing. What does it say?
5. You **don't have to** / **mustn't** walk in the park at night. It's dangerous.
6. Sally **can** / **must** play the guitar very well.

2 Complete the text with *can*, *can't*, *must*, *mustn't*, *have to* or *don't have to*.

Staying safe ONLINE

✓ You (1) _____ post personal information such as your mobile number or email address.

✓ Choose photos carefully – many people (2) _____ see or download them after you've posted them.

✓ You (3) _____ keep your privacy settings high.

✓ Don't befriend people you don't know – you (4) _____ be sure they aren't fraudsters or people who want your information.

✓ You (5) _____ change your password every week, that's not necessary – but it's a good idea to change it regularly.

✓ Respect other people's opinions! You (6) _____ agree with everyone's posts but you (7) _____ be rude.

3 Complete the sentences with *could*, *couldn't*, *had to* or *didn't have to*.

1. We _____ do the shopping because the supermarket was closed.
2. Jane saw the criminal's face, so she _____ identify him.
3. We _____ get up early yesterday because it was Sunday, so we got up late.
4. John _____ go to the hospital when he broke his arm.

Modals of deduction

4 Look at the information in the table and complete the conversation with *must*, *might* or *can't*.

	Larry	Rick	Steve
height	1.92m	1.95m	1.60m
weight	90 kilos	75 kilos	110 kilos
eyes	brown	blue	blue

Police officer: We have three suspects. Can you describe the man you saw?
Victim: He was short.
Police officer: It (1) _____ be Larry or Rick because they're tall.
Victim: The man had blue eyes.
Police officer: That (2) _____ be Rick or Steve. It (3) _____ be Larry.
Victim: The man weighed over 100 kilos.
Police officer: So the criminal (4) _____ be Larry or Rick. The criminal (5) _____ be Steve.

5 Circle the correct words.

1. A: What's that noise?
   B: I'm not sure, but it **could** / **must** be the dog.
2. It **can't** / **mustn't** be 11pm. It's light outside.
3. My friends aren't here. They **could** / **can** be at a football match.
4. There are lots of people with umbrellas. It **must** / **can't** be raining.
5. Ruth isn't at school. She **can** / **might** be at the dentist.

6 Complete the second sentence so that it has a similar meaning to the first sentence, using the word given. Do not change the word given. You must use between two and five words, including the word given.

1. I'm sure Ben isn't guilty because he was with me all day. **CAN'T**
   Ben _____ because he was with me all day.
2. I'm sure the criminals speak Russian – they live in Moscow. **MUST**
   The criminals live in Moscow so they _____.
3. It's obligatory to change your password every week. **HAS**
   Everybody _____ every week.

Grammar reference

Reported speech

direct speech	reported speech
am / is / are	➔ was / were
'We **are** on location in Chester.'	He said that they **were** on location in Chester.
present simple	➔ past simple
'The cast **work** on the film every day.'	She said that the cast **worked** on the film every day.
present continuous	➔ past continuous
'The designer **is making** the new costumes.'	She said that the designer **was making** the new costumes.
past simple	➔ past perfect
'They **translated** the subtitles.'	She said that they **had translated** the subtitles.
present perfect	➔ past perfect
'They **have recorded** the soundtrack.'	She said that they **had recorded** the soundtrack.
future: *will*	➔ *would*
'The crew **will arrive** in five minutes.'	He said that the crew **would arrive** in five minutes.
must / have to	➔ had to
'You **must** be quiet on the set.'	She said that we **had to** be quiet on the set.
can	➔ could
'I **can't** find the director.'	He said that he **couldn't** find the director.

- we use reported speech to talk about what someone else has said
- when we report speech, the tense changes
  'The storyboards **are** ready,' she said. ➔
  She said that the storyboards **were** ready.
- reported speech always needs a 'telling verb' such as *say* or *tell*
  'We started filming at 6am.' ➔
  He **said** that they had started filming at 6am.
- when we report speech, time expressions, pronouns and other words change

direct speech	reported speech
time expressions	
today ➔	that day
tomorrow ➔	the following day / the day after
next week ➔	the following week / the week after
yesterday ➔	the previous day / the day before
last week ➔	the previous week / the week before
ten years ago ➔	ten years before
this year ➔	that year
other changes	
here ➔	there
this ➔	that
these ➔	those

'My parents bought me rollerblades for my birthday **last week**,' said Sally. ➔
Sally said that her parents had bought her rollerblades for her birthday **the week before.**

Reported questions

- we make the same tense changes when we report questions as we do when we report statements
- in reported questions, the word order is the same as in affirmative statements; we do not use the auxiliary verbs *do*, *does* or *did*
- we do not use a question mark at the end of a reported question
  'What did Naomi say?' ➔
  He asked me what Naomi had said.
- to report questions with question words we use question word + subject + verb
  '**Where do** you **live**?' ➔ He asked me **where I lived**.
- we report *yes / no* questions, which do not have a question word, using *if* or *whether*
- the form is *if / whether* + subject + verb
  '**Do** you **use** social networking sites?' ➔
  He asked me **if I used** social networking sites.

Grammar exercises

Reported speech

1 Rewrite the direct speech as reported speech.

1 'I live in a big house.'
Mark said he _____ in a big house.
2 'They're watching TV.'
I said they _____ TV.
3 'I didn't see him at the beach.'
I said I _____ him at the beach.
4 'We've never been to New York.'
They said they _____ to New York.'
5 'Jack will help you.'
I said Jack _____ her.
6 'You're going to have a great time.'
She said I _____ a great time.
7 'I can't swim.'
Kate said she _____.
8 'You must tidy your room.'
My mum said I _____ my room.

2 Rewrite the sentences using reported speech.

'I can't hear you.'
Hannah said <u>she couldn't hear him.</u>
1 'We have written the subtitles.'
Matt said _____.
2 'George didn't enjoy the soundtrack.'
Alex said _____.
3 'You're doing the storyboard too slowly, you have to do it faster.'
The director said _____.
4 'We'll put on your make-up in five minutes.'
The make-up artist said _____.

3 Look at the time expressions. How do they change in reported speech?

1 today _____
2 tomorrow _____
3 yesterday _____
4 next week _____
5 last week _____
6 two years ago _____
7 this year _____
8 here _____

4 Rewrite the phone message using reported speech.

'Hi Joanne! It's Julian. I forgot to tell you the news yesterday. Ben's got a part in a film and they're filming next month! Mark's going to have a surprise party for Ben this weekend at his house. We organized it two days ago. I'll tell you all about it tomorrow.'

That was Julian. He'd forgotten to tell _____
_____
_____
_____
_____
_____

Reported questions

5 Rewrite the questions using reported speech.

1 What are your friends doing?
He asked me _____.
2 Did you see the crew last night?
The director asked me _____.
3 Have you ever helped with the lighting before?
Dan asked Mike _____.
4 What languages can you speak?
The teacher asked me _____.
5 Where do we have to go tomorrow?
I asked the director _____.

6 Complete the second sentence so that it has a similar meaning to the first sentence, using the word given. Do not change the word given. You must use between two and five words, including the word given.

'Leave quietly and shut the door.' **TOLD**
He <u>told me to leave</u> quietly and shut the door.
1 'Did you go to see that film I told you about?' **ASKED**
My friend _____ to see that film she'd told me about.
2 'We'll organize another course next week, if you want.' **OFFERED**
They _____ another course the following week if we wanted.
3 'I'd come back another time if I were you.' **ADVISED**
She _____ another time.

Grammar reference

Relative pronouns

people	places	things
who	where	which
that		that
whose		

- relative pronouns are used for giving extra information about people, places and things. They can be used to link two sentences.
  That's the man. He lives on my street.
  *That's the man **who** lives on my street.*
- the relative pronoun is the subject of the clause so we do not repeat the subject
  That's the girl. She's in my class.
  That's the girl who ~~she~~ is in my class. ✗
- the relative pronoun comes after the noun it describes
- we use *who* to talk about people
  *That's the footballer **who** scored the goal.*
- we use *whose* to talk about possession
  *There's the athlete **whose** autograph I've got.*
- we use *where* to talk about places
  *Brazil is a country **where** football is really popular.*
- we use *which* to talk about things
  *That's the advert **which** makes me laugh.*
- we can also use *that* for people and things
  *She's the girl **that** I saw yesterday in the park.*
  *Here's the book **that** I told you about.*

Indefinite pronouns

some-, *any-*, *no-* compounds			
	people	places	things
+	someone	somewhere	something
-	no one	nowhere	nothing
- / ?	anyone	anywhere	anything

- we add *-one* to talk about people, *-where* to talk about places and *-thing* to talk about things
- we use compounds with *some-* in affirmative sentences
  *I want to live **somewhere** with no adverts in the streets.*
- we use *any-* in both negative sentences and questions
  *I haven't bought **anything** this week.*
  *Has **anyone** seen that new advert?*

- we use *no-* with affirmative verbs, but the meaning is negative
  No one *I know watches adverts online.*
  (= I don't know anyone who watches adverts online)
  *There's **nowhere** in the UK without internet now.*
  (= There isn't anywhere without internet)
  *There's **nothing** I want to watch on TV.*
  (= There isn't anything I want to watch on TV)

Reflexive pronouns

singular	
I	myself
you	yourself
he	himself
she	herself
it	itself
plural	
we	ourselves
you	yourselves
they	themselves

- we use reflexive pronouns with certain verbs, for example *assert, behave, buy, convince, cut, earn, enjoy, express, help, hurt, look after, look at, respect, talk to, teach, turn off*
  *I enjoyed **myself** at the festival.*
  *He looked at **himself** in the mirror.*

Grammar exercises

UNIT 8

Relative pronouns

1 Match the sentence beginnings with the endings.

1 That's the student __
2 It was about midnight __
3 These are the boots __
4 My bedroom is the only place __
5 I've just seen the tennis player __

a) where I can be on my own.
b) whose shoes are famous.
c) who dropped out of university.
d) which my dad gave me for my birthday.
e) when I left the party.

2 Complete the sentences with *who, which, when, whose* or *where*.

1 The first day of primary school was _____ I met my best friend.
2 Those are the bins _____ we recycle our rubbish.
3 That's my brother's friend _____ got into trouble with the police.
4 A myth is a story _____ includes heroes and magic.
5 Sally is the girl _____ brother is in my class.
6 Brick Lane is a fantastic place in London _____ you can find clothes by young British designers.
7 Alice Walker is a blogger _____ writes about social problems.

Indefinite pronouns

3 Complete the sentences with the words in the box.

> anything   anywhere   no one
> nowhere   someone   something

1 I can't find my keys _____.
2 Nathan was upset because _____ tried his cake.
3 I need _____ to wear for a wedding.
4 While I was having a shower, _____ phoned me.
5 My favourite place is my home. There's _____ better.
6 I'm hungry. Have you got _____ to eat?

4 Complete the dialogue with the correct indefinite pronouns.

Ben: Hi Dave, are you going (1) _____ this weekend?
Dave: No, I've been really busy. I just want to relax and do (2) _____! What about you? Are you doing (3) _____?
Ben: I'm not sure. I'd like to do (4) _____ special. It's my girlfriend's birthday. I'd like to take her (5) _____ nice for a meal.
Dave: What about Marco's? It's a really great Italian restaurant.
Ben: That's a good idea, but I haven't got (6) _____ smart to wear.
Dave: Don't worry. I can lend you (7) _____ to wear.
Ben: Thanks, Dave!

Reflexive pronouns

5 Complete the sentences with the correct reflexive pronouns.

1 Have you ever cut _____ while you were cooking something?
2 Do your parents enjoy _____ when they go out?
3 Has your mother ever taught _____ to do anything?

6 Complete the second sentence so that it has a similar meaning to the first sentence, using the word given. Do not change the word given. You must use between two and five words, including the word given.

> We have only just started at this school so we don't have any friends yet. **ANYONE**
> We're new here so we're *not friends with anyone* yet.

1 Anya is the kindest person I know. **ANYONE**
   I don't know _____ than Anya.
2 You see that girl over there – I'm using her computer. **WHOSE**
   That's the girl _____.
3 He looked everywhere, but he couldn't find his phone. **ANYWHERE**
   He searched all over the place for his phone, but he _____.

Grammar reference

Present and past tenses

present simple
I **study** English twice a week.
Kathy **doesn't study** French.
Do you **study** Spanish?

present continuous
Mark **is revising** for his exams now.
They **aren't doing** the test today.
Are you **studying** French this year?

present perfect
I **have** just **finished** all my exams.
Sam **hasn't started** his exams yet.
Have you ever **asked** a question in class?

past simple
I **studied** for this exam last week.
Kathy **didn't study** much.
Did you **study** Spanish last year?

past continuous
Mark **was doing** an exam at this time yesterday.
They **weren't answering** the questions.
Were they **working** at home yesterday?

past perfect
The exam **had** already **started** when I arrived.
I **hadn't finished** the last question when we had to stop.
Had you already **answered** that question before?

used to
I **used to** go to a different school before I moved here.
I **didn't use to** wear a uniform, but now I have one.
Did you **use to** go to school by bus?

Future tenses

will / won't
I**'ll go** to university in September.
Sam **won't pass** the exam.
Will you **work** harder next year?

be going to
I'm **going to** train to be a teacher.
They **aren't going to** learn another language.
Is he **going to** go to university?

present continuous
We **aren't leaving** until Tuesday.

present simple
The train **leaves** at 9am.

might
I **might not** have a gap year, I **might get** a job.

future continuous
The class **will be finishing** in ten minutes.
We **won't be taking** the test tomorrow.
Will you **be taking** a gap year?

Conditionals

first conditional
If you **study** hard, you**'ll pass** the exam.

second conditional
If we **asked** the teacher, she **would explain** it again.

third conditional
If he **had wanted** the job, he **would have applied**.

Reported speech

- we use reported speech to talk about what someone else has said
- reported speech always needs a 'telling verb' such as *say* or *tell*
- when we report speech, the tense changes
- time expressions and other words also change
  'I bought these shoes here yesterday,' said the customer. ➔ *The customer said that she had bought those shoes there the day before/the previous day.*

The passive

present simple passive
GCSE exams **are taken** by all students in Year 11.

past simple passive
Uniforms **were introduced** in our school two years ago.

future passive: will
The film **will be released** next year.

- in active sentences, the subject is the person or thing that *does* the action
- in passive sentences, the subject is the person or thing that *receives* the action of the verb

Grammar exercises

Present and past tenses

1 Complete the sentences with the correct form of the verbs.

1. Some of my friends _____ abroad every summer. (go)
2. I _____ a new pair of sandals at the moment. (wear)
3. I never _____ non-fiction. I prefer fantasy and science fiction. (read)
4. It _____ (be) a beautiful day. The sun _____ (shine).
5. While the students _____ (do) the exercise, the teacher _____ (draw) a table on the board.

Future tenses

2 Circle the correct words.

1. He **'ll probably be / 's probably being / 's probably been** an engineer when he leaves university.
2. I **visited / have visited / had visited** Madrid but I **didn't go / haven't been / hadn't been** to Bilbao yet.
3. The train **leaves / 's leaving / 'll leave** at 9am tomorrow.
4. We **had / have had / had had** to walk home last night because the last bus **already left / has already left / had already left**.
5. I **'ll start / 'm going to start / start** university next year. At least, that's my plan!
6. At this time tomorrow, we **'ll sit / 're sitting / 'll be sitting** on the beach.
7. When I'm older, I think I **'ll travel / 'm travelling / travel** around the world.
8. He **didn't ride / hasn't ridden / hadn't ridden** his bike since he **had / has had / had had** an accident.

Conditionals

3 Complete the conditional sentences with the correct form of the verbs in brackets.

1. What _____ (you / buy) if you had more money?
2. If you _____ (not go) to university, what will you do?
3. You wouldn't have problems remembering things if you _____ (learn) these memory techniques.
4. I _____ (do) better at school if we had had continual assessment instead of exams.

Reported speech

4 Rewrite the direct speech as reported speech.

1. 'Jason will wait for you at the station.'
   Kate told me that _____.
2. 'By the time I finished the marathon I was exhausted.'
   Matt said that _____.
3. 'I'm going to take my driving test next week.'
   Amanda said that _____.
4. 'Do you want to visit New York this summer?'
   Emily asked me _____.

The passive

5 Complete the text with the correct passive form of the verbs in brackets.

Intelligence (1) _____ (study) by many psychologists. Years ago, it (2) _____ (believe) that people only had one type of intelligence. Then in 1983, the theory of multiple intelligences (3) _____ (develop) by Howard Gardner. In this theory, nine different types of intelligence (4) _____ (identify) – linguistic, logical–mathematical and so on. A mix of all the intelligences (5) _____ (possess) by each person, but some are stronger than others. Schools try to develop all the intelligences, but perhaps in the future other skills (6) _____ (teach) to develop them more fully. Then all the intelligences (7) _____ (use) equally by everyone.

6 Complete the second sentence so that it has a similar meaning to the first sentence, using the word given. Do not change the word given. You must use between two and five words, including the word given.

1. When we lived in Africa I had mango for breakfast every day. **USED**
   I _____ for breakfast every day when we lived in Africa.
2. Their aeroplane landed two seconds ago. **JUST**
   Their flight _____ arrived.
3. We met when we were children. **KNOWN**
   I _____ I was a child.
4. I'm pretty sure you will like my sister. **GET ON**
   You will probably _____.

Advance your vocabulary

STARTER

Holidays

1. _____
2. _____
3. _____
4. _____
5. _____
6. _____
7. _____
8. _____

1 Check the meaning of the words and expressions in the box. Listen and repeat. 🔊 31

accommodation	set off (on a journey)
check in	sunbathe
destination	take off (aeroplane)
hire a bike	take a guided tour
hotel reception	tourist brochures
land (aeroplane)	unpack

2 Look at the pictures and label them with expressions in exercise 1.

3 Circle the correct words.

1. I always feel nervous before the aeroplane **sets off / takes off**, but once I'm in the air, I'm fine.
2. There's often a lot of useful information in tourist **brochures / attractions**.
3. I think **hiring a bike / sunbathing** is a good way to explore a new place and get to know it.
4. I like to **unpack / land** as soon as I arrive and take my things out of suitcase, so I know where they are.
5. I always get to the airport early and **check in / unpack** several hours before my flight.
6. I enjoy beach holidays the most. **Taking sun / Sunbathing** is very relaxing.
7. Oxford is a popular tourist **destination / accommodation**.
8. The train **lands / arrives** in Barcelona at 12 o'clock.

4 Complete the text with words from exercise 1.

I don't like making lots of plans before I ___set off___, but my sister Julie is the opposite. When we know where we're going, she spends lots of time online finding out everything she can about the (1) _____. She downloads (2) _____ and maps and reads articles online to discover what the tourist attractions are in the area. She also chooses our (3) _____ very carefully. I like camping, but Julie prefers staying in hotels and she likes to find the best one. As soon as our flight (4) _____, Julie puts her headphones on and starts learning phrases in the language of the place we are going to. By the time we land at the airport, she can say lots of useful things! She uses the GPS on her phone to find the best route from the airport to the hotel and she asks for a map at the (5) _____ when we arrive so she can start getting to know the area. After we (6) _____ our bags, Julie likes to go out and explore the area on foot or (7) _____. I like doing this too. I prefer it to taking (8) _____, but Julie likes to do both!

5 Answer the questions so they are true for you. Write full sentences.

1. Where do you like going on holiday?
   _____
2. What kind of accommodation do you usually stay in when you're on holiday?
   _____
3. Do you like flying? What is your favourite way to travel?
   _____
4. What would your ideal holiday be? Where would you go? What would you do?
   _____

Advance your vocabulary

Blogging and vlogging

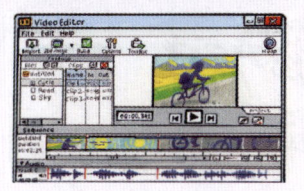

1 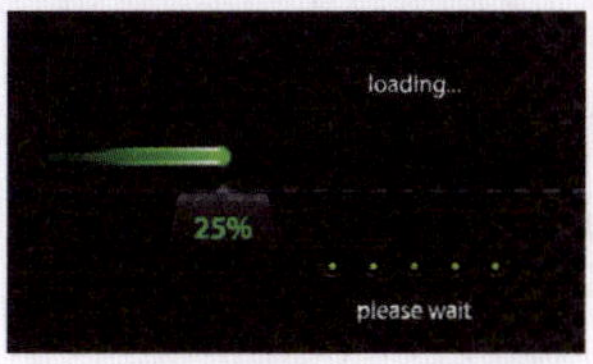 _____ 2 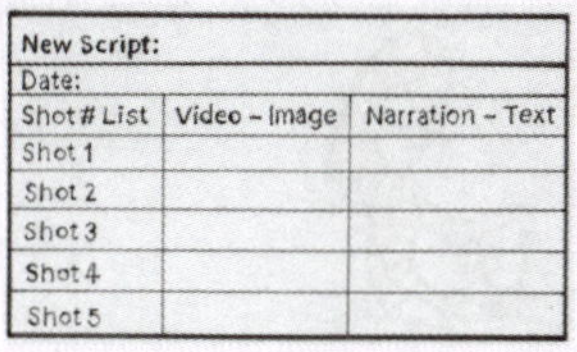 _____ 3 _____

4  _____ 5 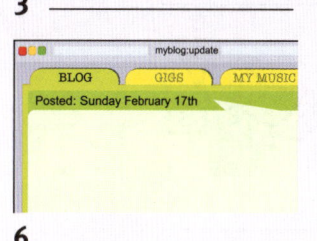 _____ 6 _____

1 Read the expressions in the box and tick the ones you know. Check the meaning of the other expressions. Listen and repeat. 🔊 32

- ☐ edit a video
- ☐ have a vlog channel
- ☐ leave a comment
- ☐ publish a blog post
- ☐ record a video
- ☐ subscribe to a channel / blog
- ☐ transcribe a video
- ☐ update your blog / vlog
- ☐ upload a photo
- ☐ write a blog
- ☐ write a caption
- ☐ write a script

2 Look at the pictures and label them with expressions from exercise 1. Which expressions can't you see?

3 Circle the correct words.

1 I read the blog and then left a **comment** / **photo** telling the writer my opinion.
2 I've got a blog and I **update** / **download** it once a week with all my news.
3 I wrote a **caption** / **blog** for each of the photos in my new post.
4 The blog looked really boring, so I **transcribed** / **uploaded** some photos onto it to make it more attractive.
5 I'm watching a video about how to publish a **post** / **comment** in a blog.
6 I started my blog a year ago. Over a hundred people **leave** / **subscribe** to it now.

4 Complete the text with words from exercise 1.

TIPS FOR VLOGGING

A vlog is a blog with videos. Some people have their own vlog (1) _____ on sites like YouTube. Here are our tips.

- Use a good camera with high sound quality to (2) _____ the videos for your vlog.
- Keep the video short – nobody wants to watch a long boring video! (3) _____ it so it contains only the best parts. There are some good free programmes you can use.
- Write a (4) _____ before you make the video. Then you will know what to say and you won't forget any important information.
- Not everyone can watch vlogs, so it's a good idea to (5) _____ your videos too. Then people can read all the information in your vlog. It's a good way to keep people following it.

5 Answer the questions so they are true for you. Write full sentences.

1 How often do you leave comments on blogs?
_____
2 Do you read any blogs? Which topics do you enjoy reading about?
_____
3 Which is your favourite YouTube channel? Why?
_____
4 Have you watched any good vlogs? What were they about?
_____

Advance your vocabulary

Unit 2

First aid

1 _____
2 _____
3 _____
4 _____
5 _____
6 _____

1 Check the meaning of the expressions in the box. Listen and repeat. 🔊 33

bandage	clean a wound
be in a coma	faint
bite	give CPR
bleed	have a heart attack
burn	have stitches
choke	take someone's pulse

2 Look at the pictures and label them with words and phrases in exercise 1. Which expressions can't you see?

3 Circle the correct words. Then do the quiz.

How good are your first aid skills?

1 If someone is **choking / bleeding** on some food, do you
  a hit him / her hard five times between the shoulders?
  b tell him / her to drink some water?
2 A friend has cut her arm badly and it is **bleeding / burning** a lot. Do you
  a give her an aspirin?
  b apply pressure to the wound?
3 You are cooking and you **burn / bandage** your arm. Do you
  a apply butter to it?
  b put it under cold running water for ten minutes?
4 Your friend is pale and you think she might **faint / coma**. Do you tell her to
  a lie down with her feet up?
  b go outside for some fresh air?
5 You have a **bite / choke** from a dog. Do you
  a clean the wound and then go to hospital?
  b panic? What if it has rabies?

Quiz answers: 1 a 2 b 3 b 4 a 5 a
4–5 correct – you are a good person to know in an emergency!
2–3 correct – you know a little about first aid. What about learning some more?
0–1 correct – you should do a course in first aid!

4 Complete the sentences with words and phrases in exercise 1.

1 If someone has a _____, their heart will stop. You need to _____. It stands for Cardio Pulmonary Resuscitation.
2 To _____, put two fingers on an artery, for example in the neck or wrist. Then count the number of beats per minute.
3 If you have a very deep cut or wound, then you have to _____. A doctor or nurse will take them out after the wound has healed.
4 When you sprain your ankle, you need to _____ it to give it support.
5 People who are _____ can still hear although they can't speak or move. This is why visitors talk or sing to them.
6 When you cut yourself with paper, it will often _____ a lot!

5 Answer the questions so they are true for you. Write full sentences.

1 Have you or one of your friends ever fainted? What happened?
_____
2 Have you or one of your friends ever burnt yourself? What happened?
_____
3 Would you like to do a course in first aid? Why (not)?
_____
4 Have you ever helped in an accident? What happened?
_____

Advance your vocabulary

UNIT 3

Volunteering

1 _____
2 _____ 
3 _____ 
4 _____ 
5 _____ 
6 _____ 
7 _____ 
8 _____ 

1 Check the meaning of the expressions in the box. Listen and repeat. 🔊 34

> campaign
> charity
> coach sports
> do a sponsored walk
> help at an animal shelter
> hold a cake sale
> mentor young people
> non-profit organization
> organize a talent show
> raise money
> take part in a conservation project
> work in a charity shop

2 Look at the pictures and label them with expressions from exercise 1. Which expressions can't you see?

3 Complete the sentences with words from exercise 1.

1 The Worldwide Fund for Nature is a _____ that helps animals.
2 A _____ works to help people in some way, rather than to make a profit.
3 Many people try to _____ for charity by doing different activities that people pay them for.
4 A _____ is a series of actions to produce social or political change.

4 Complete the text with words from exercise 1.

Giving back

Volunteering is a great way to give back to the community, meet people and learn new skills. So what sort of things can you do? If you like being active, you can (1) _____ sports. If you like helping people, then you could (2) _____. This involves sharing your experience and knowledge and giving support. Another idea is to (3) _____. You help customers or organize the things that people donate. If you like pets, then why not offer to (4) _____? If you want to help the environment, then taking part in a (5) _____ could be for you.

Of course, you don't have to volunteer regularly to give back – you could organize an event to raise money. For example, if you like cooking, then why not (6) _____? Are you musical? Then (7) _____ at your school and ask people to pay to enter it. Finally, you could (8) _____ or swim with a group of friends and ask people to give you money for each kilometre.

5 Answer the questions so they are true for you. Write full sentences.

1 Would you like to mentor a young person? Why (not)?
_____
2 Have you ever done a sponsored walk or swim? If not, would you like to? Why (not)?
_____
3 Have you ever volunteered? What did you do?
_____
4 What is your favourite charity or non-profit organization? Why?
_____

UNIT 4

Advance your vocabulary

Feelings

1 _____
2 _____ 
3 _____ 
4 _____ (Phew!) 
5 _____ (I'm ready for a challenge!)
6 _____

1 Read the words in the box and tick the ones you know. Check the meaning of the other words. Listen and repeat. 🔊 35

☐ angry ☐ panicky
☐ embarrassed ☐ pleased
☐ enthusiastic ☐ relieved
☐ heart broken ☐ scared
☐ jealous ☐ stressed
☐ moody ☐ upset

2 Look at the pictures and label them with words from exercise 1. Which words can't you see?

3 Circle the correct words.

1 John was really **jealous / scared** when he heard that Kathy had a new boyfriend.
2 Tom felt very **relieved / stressed** because he had such a lot of work to do for the next day.
3 Sally is very **scared / angry** of trying new things. She worries about everything.
4 When she didn't win the competition, Janet felt very **pleased / upset**.
5 Rob is really **moody / embarrassed** – he becomes angry and unhappy for no reason.
6 It was night and I was lost on the mountain! I felt really **enthusiastic / panicky**.
7 She was so **embarrassed / pleased** that she turned red.
8 My parents were really **pleased / moody** with my excellent exam results.

4 Complete the text with words from exercise 1.

What's the best or worst thing that's ever happened to you? Tell us about it!

I deleted my project from the computer! Luckily, my sister is good at IT. She helped me recover it. I was so (1) _____!
Julia, 16

I was really (2) _____ when I passed all my exams because I studied very hard. My parents took me out to celebrate.
Oscar, 15 ☺

I was trying to impress a boy I like but I wasn't looking where I was going and I fell over. I was really (3) _____!
Sonia, 17

My brother broke my phone. I was so (4) _____!
David, 16

My girlfriend broke up with me yesterday. I'm (5) _____.
SadBoy, 17 ☹☹☹

I volunteer for a charity and the manager told me everyone loves working with me because I'm so (6) _____. I'm really interested in the work and I love helping!
Carla, 16

5 Complete the sentences so they are true for you.

1 I'm enthusiastic about _____.
2 I feel angry when _____.
3 Before an exam I usually feel _____.
4 I don't usually feel _____.

Advance your vocabulary

UNIT 5

The invention process

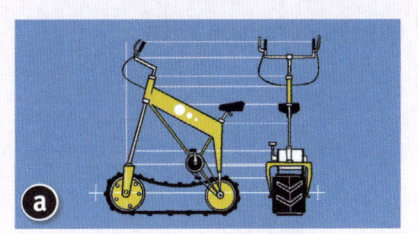

a. design a prototype 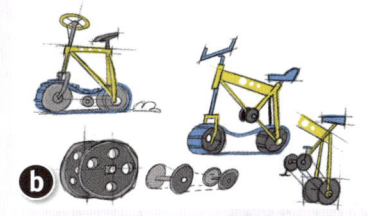
b. develop an idea 
c. win an award
d. do research 
e. look for an investor  
f. test a protype

1 Read the words in the box and tick the ones you know. Check the meaning of the other words. Listen and repeat. 🔊 36

- ☐ design a prototype
- ☐ develop an idea
- ☐ do research
- ☐ find a manufacturer
- ☐ get a patent
- ☐ improve the design
- ☐ look for an investor
- ☐ produce a prototype
- ☐ solve technical problems
- ☐ test a prototype
- ☐ win an award
- ☐ write a business plan

2 Match the steps a–f of the invention process in the pictures with sentences 1–6.

1 The development team can do research in a testing lab. ___
2 Before they can spend lots of money, the development team needs to look for an investor. ___
3 If the protoype is tested, the designers learn what works and what needs to be improved. ___
4 A precise technical drawing is drawn to scale with a front and a side view. ___
5 Maybe you'll win an award if your invention process is successful. ___
6 Lots of small sketches are drawn to develop an idea – they are not drawn to scale. ___

3 Complete the text with words from exercise 1.

Success!

Ross Fobian, 29, is a successful young British entrepreneur. In 2008 he decided to start a new business with Richard Hamnett. Ross had an idea for a business to develop software that allows big companies to see what customers do and look for on their website. He didn't do any (1) _____ because he was sure his idea would work. First, he had to (2) _____ the idea. Then he and Richard had to (3) _____ and produce a prototype programme. After that they had to (4) _____ the prototype to ensure it worked. There were a few problems so they had to (5) _____ the design of the programme. They called the business ResponseTap and several big companies soon became investors. The business is now doing really well – they may even (6) _____ for it!

4 Answer the questions so they are true for you. Write full sentences.

1 Do you know anyone who has won an award for an invention? What for?
_____
2 Is it important to write a business plan? Why (not)?
_____
3 If you could have your own business, what would it be?
_____
4 What young entrepreneurs do you know about in your country?
_____

UNIT 6 Advance your vocabulary

Managing money

Speech bubbles:
- I want to bring this back.
- OK, here's your money back. (a)
- I've only got £5. (b)
- Here's £5, but you have to give it back tomorrow. (c)

1 Read the words in the box and tick the ones you know. Check the meaning of the other words. Listen and repeat. 🔊 37

☐ borrow   ☐ lend
☐ budget   ☐ owe
☐ deposit   ☐ pay for
☐ donate   ☐ refund
☐ earn   ☐ save
☐ get a bank loan ☐ spend
☐ invest   ☐ withdraw

2 Match people a–g in the pictures with sentences 1–7.

1 He's borrowing some money. __
2 She's refunding some money. __
3 She's withdrawing some money. __
4 He's paying for something. __
5 She's lending some money. __
6 He's earning some money. __
7 She's donating some money. __

3 Match words and expressions 1–6 with definitions a–f.

1 owe   __
2 get a bank loan __
3 invest   __
4 budget   __
5 spend   __
6 deposit   __

a) use money to pay for things
b) plan the way you will spend the money you have so you don't spend too much
c) when you have to give someone an amount of money because you bought something from them or you borrowed money from them
d) when the bank gives you money to buy something, eg a car
e) pay money into a bank account
f) use your money with the intention of making a profit from it, eg by buying shares

4 Complete the text with words from exercise 1.

Managing your money

Managing your money is a life skill, but unfortunately most young people don't learn it at school! So what do you need to know?

- It's a good idea to regularly (1) _____ some money. It's not a good idea to keep it under your bed – you should open a bank account and (2) _____ your money there.
- You should learn to (3) _____ your money. Each month, calculate how much money you have and what you can (4) _____ it on.
- You can get a part-time job to (5) _____ some money, then you can buy the extra things you want.
- It's never a good idea to (6) _____ money to people. Always repay the money you borrow.
- It's also good to (7) _____ money to charity and buy presents for other people – don't just spend it on yourself!

5 Complete the sentences so they are true for you.

1 I usually spend my money on _____.
2 Once I saved up to buy _____.
3 Last week I paid for _____.
4 In my opinion _____ is the best thing to invest money in.

Advance your vocabulary

Television

1 _____
2 _____ 
3 _____ 
4 _____ 
5 _____ 
6 _____ 

1 Read the words in the box and tick the ones you know. Check the meaning of the other words. Listen and repeat. 🔊 38

- [ ] breaking news
- [ ] broadcast
- [ ] channel
- [ ] couch potato
- [ ] live coverage
- [ ] on air
- [ ] presenter
- [ ] prime time
- [ ] remote control
- [ ] rerun
- [ ] viewer
- [ ] viewing figures

2 Look at the pictures and label them with expressions from exercise 1.

3 Complete the sentences with the correct form of words from exercise 1.

1. I love watching _____ of series that were first on TV years ago.
2. The show is _____ live from the studio every day. It's _____ now.
3. They took the series off TV because the _____ were really low. Not many people watched it at all. _____ who watched it said it was boring.
4. A _____ is someone who spends a lot of time at home watching TV.

4 Complete the text with the correct form of words from exercise 1.

What's on

There are so many (1) _____ on TV it's hard to know which one to watch! Our free guide can help you choose the best ones for you.

Do you want to watch a (2) _____ of an old popular TV series such as *Buffy*? Then Channel 52 is for you – it has hundreds of old series to choose from.

Sport special has (3) _____ of all the top sports events. Tonight, it's showing the football match between Arsenal and Manchester United.

CNN is an American news channel – watch it for (4) _____ stories and reports.

Wildlife Special is for animal lovers. Watch talented (5) _____ such as David Attenborough or Bear Grylls and learn all about animals and the environment.

Film fans will love Film 24. It shows all the latest films, as well as classics, 24 hours a day – even during (6) _____ TV (8pm – 11pm). And there are no adverts to interrupt your viewing so you won't ever need the (7) _____ to change channel!

5 Complete the sentences so they are true for you.

1. I sometimes watch reruns such as _____.
2. During prime time I watch _____.
3. My favourite channel is _____ because _____.
4. I think live coverage of sports and other events is _____.
5. My favourite TV presenter is _____. I like him / her because _____.

UNIT 8 Advance your vocabulary

The media

1 _____   2 _____   3 _____   4 _____

5 _____   6 _____   7 _____   8 _____

1 Check the meaning of the words in the box. Listen and repeat. ♪) 39

24-hour news channel	journalist
broadsheet	paparazzi
circulation	phone-in
editor	photographer
eye-witness report	press conference
headline	tabloid

2 Look at the pictures and label them with expressions from exercise 1.

3 Complete the table with words from exercise 1. Some words can go in more than one column.

People	Things related to newspapers	Things related to TV or radio
_____	_____	_____
_____	_____	_____
_____	_____	_____
_____	_____	_____
_____	_____	_____
_____	_____	_____

4 Complete the text with the correct form of words from exercise 1.

HOME | NEWS | SPORTS | SHARE

In the news

The most serious (1) _____ want to work for a (2) _____ because they have 'real' news – interesting articles and top international news stories. The (3) _____ newspapers are full of stories about celebrities!

Creating a news article is hard work. First, journalists have to find a good story. Then they do some research and interview any (4) _____ (the people who saw the events). They write down good quotes to use. A (5) _____ will go with the journalist to take pictures of the people and places involved in the story. Then the journalist writes the article and sends it to the (6) _____. He or she decides whether to include the story or not and then makes any corrections. Often the editor and journalist decide on the (7) _____ for the story together. How do editors decide which stories to include? The (8) _____ figures are very important, so they choose stories that they think will make people buy the newspaper.

5 Answer the questions so they are true for you. Write full sentences.

1 Would you like to be a journalist? Why (not)?
_____

2 Do you listen to the radio? Why (not)?
_____

3 Do you only read the headlines or do you read everything in a newspaper? Why?
_____

4 Do you prefer broadsheet or tabloid newspapers? Why?
_____

Advance your vocabulary

UNIT 9

Further study and the world of work

1 _____

2 _____

3 _____

I worked with John Minty for three years. At all times I have found John to be dependable and hard-working. I am happy to provide further information if required.
Yours faithfully,
Katherine Taylor
Katherine Taylor

4 _____

Come and learn how to make a music video!
July 1–22
Experienced tutors & professional camera operators
Cost: £525

5 _____

1 Check the meaning of the words in the box. Listen and repeat. ♪) 40

> apprentice   intern
> apprenticeship   internship
> distance learning   lecturer
> employee   qualification
> employer   reference
> evening classes   vocational course

2 Look at the pictures and label them with expressions from exercise 1. Which expressions can't you see?

3 Complete the sentences with words from exercise 1.

1 The biscuit factory is my town's biggest _____. It has over 1,000 _____ that work there.
2 Joe is a _____ at York University. He teaches linguistics.
3 Jamie did an _____ to learn to be a carpenter. He didn't go to college to study carpentry – he learned from a carpenter. He was an _____.
4 I finished my degree in law two months ago and I'm doing an _____ in a law firm in London. I'm an _____ there.

4 Complete the text with words from exercise 1.

Helpline
We answer your questions about studying and work.

I'm leaving school in June. I'd like a job related to sports but I don't want to go to university. Any advice?
Matt

@Matt – Yes! How about going to a teacher training college and getting a (1) _____ as a sports teacher?

I've just applied for my first job, but they want a (2) _____. Who can I ask for one?
Sharon

@Sharon – Why don't you ask one of your teachers? They can write about your character and how well you study.

5 Answer the questions so they are true for you. Write full sentences.

1 Would you prefer to go to university or do a vocational course? Why?
   _____
2 Do you think internships and apprenticeships are a good idea? Why (not)?
   _____
3 Have you ever done any distance learning or evening classes? What did you study?
   _____

Writing hub

UNIT 1

Text type: A personal blog

Circus Time!
Welcome to my blog!

Hello! I'm Ellie and this is my blog. This year has been pretty exciting because I decided to learn some new skills. I started at circus school in September and I've already learned a lot – and I've made some great friends. I go every Saturday for the whole day. Here's my story ...

12 October, 17:35   Juggling isn't easy

Juggling was the first thing we started to learn. We've had two days of classes since the course started. I've dropped the balls hundreds of times!!! I've also practised a lot ... I was a bit scared of looking stupid when I started, but now I'm quite confident. I can juggle with three balls – hooray! I haven't learned to juggle with four balls yet – that's the next step!

29 October, 22:14   Success!!

I've just got home from my first public performance! It went very well – I juggled with four balls and I didn't make any mistakes. My friend Tom started at the circus school two years ago and he did some acrobatics. He was really fantastic – I hope I can do that one day. I think everyone enjoyed all the performances. Next week I'm going to start learning to ride a unicycle. I'm looking forward to it ...

I've posted some more photos – check them out here.

give each post a title

use adverbs of degree to show the intensity of something

use a variety of tenses (present simple, present continuous, past simple, present perfect, going to, etc) to make the blog more interesting

1 Read and listen to the blog. Then circle T (true) or F (false). 🔊 41

1. Ellie hasn't learned much at circus school yet.   T F
2. Ellie had been to two days of classes by 12 October.   T F
3. Ellie's first performance in public was a disaster.   T F
4. Ellie can juggle with four balls now.   T F
5. Ellie is planning to do acrobatics next week.   T F

2 Rewrite the sentences using the adverbs of degree in brackets.

1. Rob is confident. (not very)
   _____
2. The performance was good. (pretty)
   _____
3. They were nervous about juggling. (a bit)
   _____
4. I'm happy to be at a circus school. (really)
   _____
5. The clowns are funny. (very)
   _____
6. I'm getting good at riding a unicycle. (quite)
   _____

3 Complete the text with the correct form of the verbs in brackets. Look at the time expressions to help you.

Hi! I (1) _____ (just start) my acrobatics course. Yesterday we (2) _____ (learn) about how to fall safely so you don't hurt yourself. Next Saturday we (3) _____ (practise) it! I (4) _____ (look forward) to it. We (5) _____ (not try) any activities in the air yet – that's next month. At the moment I (6) _____ (read) some tips for circus performers. All good performers (7) _____ (do) some exercise every day to stay strong. I (8) _____ (go) to the gym tomorrow!

112

Writing task

Writing a personal blog

Write a personal blog about doing a course or hobby. Choose one of the ideas from the box or use your own idea.

    drama course   skateboarding

Step 1 Plan

Complete the table with notes about the activity.

Post 1: Introduction Say what you are learning about, when you started, how often you go.	
Post 2: Say what you have done and haven't done yet and how you feel.	
Post 3: Describe an exciting part of the course or hobby and what happened. Say what you are going to do next.	

Step 2 Write

Write your first draft. Use your notes from Step 1 and the blog on page 112 to help you. Remember to give your blog a title, give each post a title and finish the blog in an interesting way.

_____
_____
_____
_____
_____
_____
_____

Step 3 Check

Check your work. Check that you have used:
- [ ] adverbs of degree
- [ ] a variety of tenses
- [ ] time expressions
- [ ] short forms and punctuation for informal writing

Finally remember to always check your:
grammar   vocabulary   spelling

Step 4 Write

Write your final copy in your notebook.

USEFUL EXPRESSIONS

I'm / We're … and this is my / our blog …
Here's my / our story …
I've just (started) …
I was a bit / quite …
I'm very / pretty / really …
At the moment …
Yesterday …
I'm looking forward to …

Writing hub

Text type: A news report

A forest fire survivor

Last summer, 17-year-old hiking enthusiast Jake Keller was with a group of ten hikers in Greece. They were walking on an island. On 17th July they set out early for a long walk up a mountain. They were looking forward to climbing the mountain and then staying the night in a village on the other side.

They had reached the base of the mountain when disaster struck. Some other hikers had started a fire for cooking, but the trees nearby caught fire. It was spreading fast because of the wind. The hikers saw the smoke. At first they weren't worried, but they soon realized they were in danger. After that they climbed up the mountain as quickly as possible to try to escape the fire. Then they waited at the top. They knew it was the safest place to stay.

Luckily, they had told the hotel owners exactly where they were going, so the authorities knew they were in danger. Eventually a search and rescue helicopter found them. By the time the helicopter picked them up, the fire had almost reached them. They were exhausted and scared. The paramedics gave them first aid for minor injuries, but luckily they were all fine. They were delighted to survive their terrifying experience.

Annotations:
- use the past continuous, past simple and past perfect to show when events happened
- use connectors of sequence to show the order things happened
- use eventually, finally or in the end to say what happened at the end of a long sequence of events
- use extreme adjectives to make your writing more interesting

1 Read and listen to the news report. Order the events. 🔊 42

- a Some other hikers started a fire.
- b Jake's group realized they were in danger.
- c A helicopter found the group.
- d Jake's group started their hike up the mountain.
- e Paramedics treated their injuries.
- f Jake's group saw the smoke from the fire.
- g Jake and his friends went to an island.
- h Jake's group reached the bottom of the mountain.
- i Jake's group told the hotel owners where they were going.
- j Jake's group quickly climbed to the top of the mountain.
- k The helicopter took the group to safety.

2 Match the paragraphs 1–3 with descriptions a–c.

a) describing the main events – what the disaster was, what happened
b) finishing the story – what happened in the end and how people felt
c) setting the scene – who the story is about, where and when it happened

3 Read the text and complete it with the words in the box.

at first   awful   by this time   delighted
in the end   luckily   one day   then

Snowed in!

(1) _____ last winter Lucy Hart was studying at home. Her parents had gone to visit some friends for the day. Suddenly it started to snow really hard. Soon, Lucy couldn't leave the house. (2) _____ she wasn't worried. She thought her parents would manage to get home, but after a few hours they still hadn't returned. Lucy tried to walk to the neighbour's house, but it was impossible. (3) _____ she tried to phone her parents, but she didn't get an answer. (4) _____ she was hungry, but (5) _____ there was plenty of food in the house. (6) _____ Lucy spent the night in the house and the emergency services managed to get to it the next morning. Lucy was (7) _____ her (8) _____ experience was over!

Writing task

Writing a news report

Write a news report about surviving a natural disaster. Choose one of the ideas from the box or use your own idea.

> a tornado   a tsunami   an earthquake
> a volcanic eruption

Step 1 | Plan

Think of a disaster story for a news report (the story can be invented). Complete the table with notes about the story. Then organize the report into three paragraphs. Check the model on page 114.

Who is in the story?	Where and when did it happen?	What were the main events?	What happened next? How did the people feel?	What happened in the end?

Step 2 | Write

Write your first draft. Use your notes from Step 1 and the news report on page 114 to help you.

_____
_____
_____
_____
_____
_____
_____
_____
_____
_____
_____
_____
_____

Step 3 | Check

Check your work. Check that you have used:
- [ ] connectors of sequence
- [ ] extreme adjectives
- [ ] a variety of tenses
- [ ] time expressions

Finally remember to always check your:
grammar   vocabulary   spelling

USEFUL EXPRESSIONS

Luckily, / Amazingly …
Last summer / On 2nd June …
By the time (the hurricane started), we had (reached a shelter) …
… when disaster struck.
At first …
Then / Next …
After that …
In the end …

Step 4 | Write

Write your final copy in your notebook.

UNIT 3 Writing hub

Text type: A CV

check that you have completed all the sections and that the information is relevant to the job you are applying for

make sure you include your contact details and that the information is correct

Curriculum Vitae

PERSONAL INFORMATION
Sarah Brown
24 Hough Lane, Leeds, LS4 5SK
+ 44 0113 876432
s.brown@email.com

POSITION APPLIED FOR
Work experience at Meade Activity Centre for Young People

EDUCATION AND TRAINING
September 2019–June 2020
I will be taking GCSEs in the following subjects: English language, English literature, mathematics, science, Spanish, German, ICT, history

WORK EXPERIENCE
August 2018
Monitor at international summer camp

October 2017–present
Volunteer at Oaks Youth Club

PERSONAL SKILLS
Mother tongue	English
Other language(s)	Spanish and German
Communication skills	Excellent communication skills gained as volunteer at Oaks Youth Club
Organizational skills	Excellent organizational skills
Computer skills	Proficient with Word, Excel and Acrobat
Other skills	EFR first aid certificate; Piano Grade 6; Experience in sports coaching for 6–12 year-olds.

check that all dates and information are correct

1 Read and listen to the CV. Then answer the questions. 🔊 43

1 What is Sarah applying for?
   _____
2 Has she taken her GCSEs already? How do you know?
   _____
3 What work experience does she have?
   _____
4 What languages does she speak?
   _____
5 What skills does she have that would be useful when working in an activity centre for young people?
   _____

2 What order would you put the following work experience in? Why?

☐ a October 2017 – present Volunteer at Youth Club
☐ b August 2018 Monitor at summer camp
☐ c July – August 2017 Volunteer at summer camp

3 Order the words to make entries for a CV.

1 skills / Excellent / verbal and / communication / written
   _____
2 with / Proficient / software / Macintosh
   _____
3 be / exams / I / in / following / subjects / taking / will / the
   _____
4 a volunteer / skills / organizational / Excellent / as / an after-school club / at / gained
   _____
5 at / Volunteer / an arts centre /
   _____
6 numerical / gained / skills / as / a youth club / the treasurer of / Excellent
   _____

Writing task

UNIT 3

Writing a CV

Write a CV to accompany a job application.

Step 1 Plan

Read the advert and the notes. Decide which information is relevant to include and where to put it.

Want to work in a restaurant?

We are looking for 16–18 year-olds to work weekends and evenings at Greens Restaurant as kitchen assistants and waiters. Flexible hours.

Must be organized, hard-working and be able to communicate well. Experience of working in a café or restaurant preferred, but not essential.

Kitchen assistant: Ref GG/21-A
Waiter: Ref GG/3-B

Apply for job – waiter
January – June 2013 Worked in a busy café, serving customers – good communication skills (writing and speaking)
First aid certificate
July – August 2013 Worked in a summer camp – excellent organizational skills
Piano, Grade 4
Enjoy walking and going to the cinema
September 2012 – June 2013 Worked in a supermarket putting products on shelves – very hard work!
Taking GCSE exams (English language, English literature, mathematics, science, French, History, Geography, Music)

Step 2 Write

Write your first draft. Use your notes from Step 1 and the CV on page 116 to help you.

_____
_____
_____
_____
_____
_____
_____
_____
_____
_____
_____
_____
_____

Step 3 Check

Check your work. Check that:
- [ ] the contact details, dates and information are correct
- [ ] your work experience is listed with most recent first
- [ ] you have completed all the sections
- [ ] the CV looks organized and well-presented

Finally remember to always check your:
grammar   vocabulary   spelling

USEFUL EXPRESSIONS

Excellent organizational skills gained as …
Good communication skills
I will be taking the following exams: …
Proficient with (computers / first aid)

Step 4 Write

Write your final copy in your notebook.

Writing hub

Text type: Instant messages

- use personal questions

> Hi Lisa, how's it going?

> Good! What's up?

> I've got a problem and I need some advice! My best friend Amy has started going out with a boy called Mike. Well, they get on really well, but he wants to see her ALL the time.

- use emoticons to show how you feel

> Oh no! ☹ That's SO awful. Why don't you suggest meeting up with her next weekend?

- use conditional sentences to talk about what might happen and to give advice

> I tried that last week – we were going to hang out together, but she called at the last minute and said she had to see Mike. If he asks, then she cancels her plans with me. It's so annoying! I don't want to fall out with Amy, but if I don't say anything, it'll get worse.

- use phrasal verbs when you write in an informal style

> If I were you, I'd suggest going out in a group of friends. That way you can chat to Amy and Mike will meet all your friends. I'm sure they'd agree to a fun night out with everyone.

> Yes, I hadn't thought of that! Great idea!!! They'll definitely be happy with that plan. I'll message Amy now and ask her if that's OK. Thanks Lisa!

- use everyday expressions

> Bye for now! Good luck Holly!

1 Read and listen to the instant message conversation. Then circle T (true) or F (false). 🔊 44

1. Holly is writing to Lisa for advice. T F
2. Holly's friend Amy has just broken up with her boyfriend. T F
3. Last weekend Amy cancelled her plans with Holly. T F
4. Lisa thinks Holly should meet Amy on her own. T F
5. Holly doesn't think Amy and Mike will agree to Lisa's suggestion. T F

2 Circle the correct words.

1. Why don't you **talk / talking** to your parents?
2. What about **ask / asking** your parents to pick you up?
3. You should **suggest / suggesting** going with a big group of friends.
4. I'm sure your parents **agree / would agree** with this idea.
5. I **haven't / hadn't** thought of that!
6. How about **buy / buying** the tickets online?

3 Complete the sentences with the correct form of the verbs in brackets.

> Hi Dan, how's things?

> Hi Lucy. I'm fed up!! ☹ My sister keeps borrowing my things without asking.

> If I (1) _____ (be) you, I (2) _____ (talk) to your parents.

> I've tried that, but if my parents (3) _____ (tell) my sister not to do it, she (4) _____ (be) angry! I don't want to have an argument with her.

> Perhaps your sister (5) _____ (listen) if you asked her to try and find a solution with you.

> OK, I'll try! I (6) _____ (not think) of that! I'll go and talk to her now.

> Good luck!

Writing task

UNIT 4

Writing instant messages

Write an instant message conversation about a problem.

Step 1 Plan

Read the instant message and make notes about how to answer it. Think about how you can start and finish an instant message conversation. Use conditional sentences to talk about what might happen and to give advice.
Make notes for seven more parts, four from you and three from your friend.

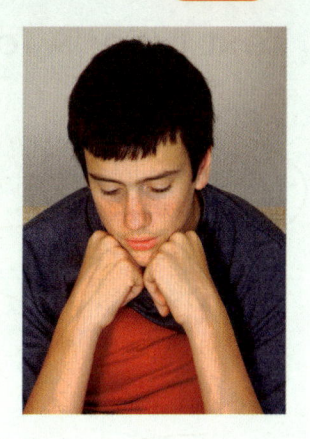

- Explaining the problem in more detail
- Ideas for solving the problem
- Useful phrases and expressions

> I'm afraid I've got a problem with our plan to go to the concert. My parents don't want me to go unless my older brother goes too!

Step 2 Write

Write your first draft. Use your notes from Step 1 and the instant message conversation on page 118.

Hi!
_____

Step 3 Check

Check your work. Check that you have used:
- [ ] everyday expressions and personal questions
- [ ] phrasal verbs
- [ ] the correct tenses in conditional sentences

Finally, remember to always check your:
grammar   vocabulary   spelling

USEFUL EXPRESSIONS

Oh no!
Why don't you … / If I were you, I'd …
What about …
I hadn't thought of that! Good idea!
Good luck!

Step 4 Write

Write your final copy in your notebook.

Writing hub

UNIT 5

Text type: A formal letter

Put your address in the top right corner → 74 Park Drive, York, YO2 4PL

put the date under your address → 14th March

put the address of the person you are writing to on the left →
The Manager
Top Computers
35 Raikes Lane
London SW2 7RR

Dear Sir or Madam,

I ordered a new tablet computer (a Gamma Pi 8 Pro at £187.50) from your website on 5th February. My order *was placed* at 18:30 and I received a confirmation email. The money was taken from my account the next day.

Unfortunately, when the tablet arrived it had been damaged and the screen was cracked. When I called your Customer Help Line, I was told that I had to send it back. I sent it back immediately, but I still haven't received a replacement.

I would appreciate it if you could send a replacement or refund my money within one week. I have never had any problems using your website before and am disappointed this has not been resolved sooner. I look forward to your reply and a quick resolution to this problem.

Yours faithfully,

Maggie Hall
Maggie Hall

use passive forms when you write in a formal style

use formal phrases

use the correct closing phrase to match the opening greeting

put your signature and write or print your name clearly below

---

1 Read and listen to the letter. Then answer the questions. 🔊 45

1 What did Maggie order and when?
   _____
2 What was the problem?
   _____
3 What was she told to do?
   _____
4 What does she want the manager to do?
   _____

2 Match the paragraphs 1–3 with descriptions a–c.

a) explain the problem (what it is, what has and hasn't happened about it) —
b) describe the product you are complaining about (what it is, when you bought it, how much it cost, etc) —
c) say what you want to happen (possible solutions, time frames) —

3 Complete the passive sentences with the correct form of the verbs in brackets.

1 When I spoke to Customer Services, I _____ (inform) that I would have to send the product back.
2 The money _____ (take) out of my account on 3rd April.
3 When I received it, the games console _____ (already / use).
4 I am disappointed that this problem _____ (not resolve) yet.
5 I _____ (tell) by the manager that I could have a replacement.
6 The batteries _____ (replace) yesterday, but it still doesn't work.

120

Writing task

Writing a formal letter

Write a formal letter of complaint about a product.

Step 1 Plan

Complete the table with notes about an e-reader you bought that stopped working after only a week. Check the model on page 120.

Describe the product (cost, where and when you bought it)	
Explain the problem and say what has and hasn't happened to solve the problem	
Say the solution you would like and when you want it to happen	

Step 2 Write

Write your first draft. Use your notes from Step 1 and the letter on page 120 to help you.

_____
_____
_____
_____
_____
_____
_____
_____
_____
_____
_____
_____

Step 3 Check

Check your work. Check that you have:
- [ ] used the correct layout
- [ ] started and finished the letter correctly
- [ ] used formal language
- [ ] used passive forms correctly

Finally, remember to always check your:
grammar   vocabulary   spelling

USEFUL EXPRESSIONS

To resolve the situation, ...
I would appreciate it if ...
... as quickly as possible / within a week / within five working days
I look forward to ...

Step 4 Write

Write your final copy in your notebook.

Writing hub

UNIT 6

Text type: A personal profile

Tawanda Jones

use modals of possibility and certainty

use connectors of cause and effect to talk about reasons why things happen and the results of actions

Tawanda Jones is from Camden, New Jersey, one of the poorest and most violent cities in the USA. She is the founder of Camden Sophisticated Sisters (CSS), a non-profit organization that uses dance routines and music to teach discipline and self-confidence to vulnerable young people. You *might not* recognize her because she isn't famous, but she has helped thousands of young people to graduate from high school.

Tawanda grew up in Camden. When she was just 15, she realized that many young women struggled with poverty, being different and making good choices, *so* she decided to do something about it. In 1986, she set up CSS because she wanted to help. She has also used it to help young women do well at school and to get involved in the community *because* she believes that this will make Camden a better place to live.

Tawanda's key values include a commitment to improving the lives of young people, pride in her community and a strong work ethic. Because of this, the organization has grown from the original 80 members. Over 4,000 people have participated in the scheme so far.

Tawanda is a role model and due to her leadership skills and dedication, she has made a difference to the lives of many young people and to the community. It can't be easy working in such tough conditions, but she has certainly succeeded.

Personal details

Nationality
American

Residence
Camden, New Jersey, USA

Occupation
Founder and teacher, Camden Sophisticated Sisters

---

1 Read and listen to the profile. Then answer the questions. ◆)) 46

1 What organization did Tawanda start and what are its aims?
_____

2 How has Tawanda used the organization she set up?
_____

3 What are her values?
_____

4 What has she achieved?
_____

2 Complete the texts with the verbs in the box.

> can't   doesn't have to   had to   might   might not

1 My aunt is a director in a big company. She _____ be famous, but I admire her for what she has achieved. It _____ be easy being one of the few women directors.

2 Bill Gates is very rich, so he _____ work now, but when he started his company, he _____ work extremely hard. You _____ know the story of his success because he's very famous.

3 Complete the text with the correct form of the words in brackets. Use the suffixes -*ship*, -*ance*, -*ity*, -*ion* and -*ment*.

> **Robin Emmons** looks like many other young women, but her (1) _____ (appear) is deceptive. When she learned that many people in North Carolina don't have access to healthy food, she decided to do something. She started an (2) _____ (organize) called Sow Much Good (SMG). SMG has grown 26,000 pounds of fresh vegetables for the (3) _____ (commune). This incredible (4) _____ (achieve) is due to her (5) _____ (leader) skills and (6) _____ (commit). It is an amazing success, which can't have been easy.

Writing task

Writing a personal profile

Write a profile of a person you admire.

Step 1 Plan

Read the information about Chad Pregracke and look at the description outline. Decide which paragraph each fact should be in.

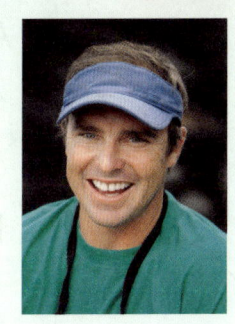

Description outline	Facts
Paragraph 1: introduction Who the person is and why you are writing about them	☐ enthusiastic and strong work ethic
	☐ set up a non-profit organization – Living Lands and Waters (LLW)
Paragraph 2: Career development Details about his / her career	☐ strong commitment to making rivers cleaner and safer
	☐ an environmentalist – he cleans up the Mississippi River and other rivers in America
Paragraph 3: Values and achievements What his / her values are and how these have helped him / her achieve his / her goals Important achievements	☐ 1997 – got a grant to start cleaning the Mississippi River and worked alone to remove 45,000 pounds of rubbish
	☐ 2007 – LLW started a new programme to plant trees along rivers
	☐ became interested in helping river communities
Paragraph 4: Conclusion Summary Your opinion (optional)	☐ now LLW organizes 70 clean-ups a year in 50 different communities
	☐ great leadership skills and dedication to the project
	☐ has inspired others – over 70,000 volunteers have joined LLW

Step 2 Write

Write your first draft. Use your notes from Step 1 and the profile on page 122 to help you.

_____
_____
_____
_____
_____
_____
_____
_____

Step 3 Check

Check your work. Check that you have used:
- ☐ present and past modals
- ☐ modals of deduction
- ☐ connectors of cause and effect

Finally remember to always check your:
grammar   vocabulary   spelling

USEFUL EXPRESSIONS

You might / might not recognize him / her because …
His / Her key values include …
His / Her leadership skills …
He / She has made a difference …

Step 4 Write

Write your final copy in your notebook.

Writing hub

UNIT 7

Text type: A report

Report: A survey about films

This report outlines the results of a survey about films and young people at our school. 50 students aged 14–16 were asked about their film viewing habits and preferences.

The majority of those questioned said that they watched films on TV, online and at the cinema. The most popular types of film were comedies, sci-fi films and dramas. Only one in ten thought that films with subtitles were good. Over 80% agreed that most films were aimed at children or adults, not teenagers – a large proportion of those asked said that they would like to have more films for young people. More than half of those interviewed said that they preferred to watch films at the cinema rather than on TV because you could appreciate the soundtrack and special effects better. 30% suggested that there should be cheaper cinema tickets for young people. Almost everyone complained that films were too violent.

To sum up, this survey shows that young people watch films in different ways and that there is a lack of good films for this age group. I suggest that we send this report to local cinemas and to the TV broadcasting companies so that they can take our opinions into account.

(annotations: use different ways to express statistics; use a variety of reporting verbs)

1 Read and listen to the report. Then circle T (true) or F (false). 🔊 47

1. Comedies are not very popular. T F
2. Most people think there aren't many films for teenagers. T F
3. A lot of people are in favour of having more films for young people. T F
4. Over 50% of people prefer watching films at home. T F
5. The writer doesn't think it's worth sending the report to local cinemas. T F

2 Express the numbers in a different way.

32%   _about a third_
1. 85%   _____
2. 20%   _____
3. 10%   _____
4. 53%   _____
5. 70%   _____
6. 75%   _____
7. 98%   _____

3 Rewrite the sentences in reported speech using the reporting verbs in brackets.

1. 'I never do sport.' (he / say)
   _____
2. 'Yes, shopping is fun.' (they / agree)
   _____
3. 'There should be more facilities for young people.' (they / suggest)
   _____
4. 'There isn't a good sports centre.' (she / complain)
   _____
5. 'We usually spend time in friends' houses.' (they / say)
   _____
6. 'I will finish my book tomorrow.' (she / think)
   _____

Writing task

UNIT 7

Writing a report

Write a report explaining the results of a survey about free time.

Step 1 Plan

Look at the chart showing the results of a survey about free time answered by 1,000 students aged 15–19. Then complete the table with notes about the results.

Paragraph 1 *the introduction: who took part in the survey and what the survey was about*	
Paragraph 2 *the results of the survey*	
Paragraph 3 *the conclusion and your recommendations*	

Step 2 Write

Write your first draft. Use your notes from Step 1 and the report on page 124 to help you.

Step 3 Check

Check your work. Check that you have:
- [ ] used a variety of reporting verbs
- [ ] used the correct tenses in reported statements
- [ ] used different ways of reporting statistics

Finally remember to always check your:
grammar   vocabulary   spelling

Step 4 Write

Write your final copy in your notebook.

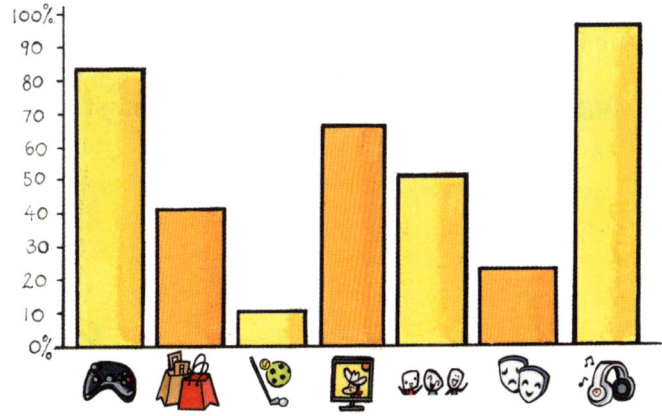

USEFUL EXPRESSIONS

This report outlines the results of a survey about …
(50) students aged (14–15) were asked about …
To sum up, this survey shows that …
I suggest that we should …

Writing hub

Text type: A for and against essay

Should there be a ban on adverts on television before 9pm?

Nowadays, children are bombarded with adverts. Many experts believe that this encourages consumerism and puts pressure on their parents to buy things they can't afford. They would like there to be no advertising on TV before 9pm, **but** there are arguments for and against this proposition.

use connectors of contrast

On the one hand, children wouldn't see adverts on TV until they were older and more able to think for themselves. As a result, they would be far less influenced by advertising. **Moreover**, if there were no adverts before 9pm, there would be more time for other programmes such as documentaries.

use connectors of addition

On the other hand, one of the main arguments against banning adverts on TV is that adverts might become more attractive to children because they couldn't see them. So, they might try to find them on the internet. In addition, companies should be able to advertise their products in order to sell them.

To sum up, I am in favour of banning all advertising on TV before 9pm. However, I believe that although this is a good idea, the most important thing is to educate children to think critically.

1 Read and listen to the essay. Then complete the table. 🔊 48

Arguments in favour	Arguments against
children wouldn't see adverts on TV until they were older and more able to think for themselves	

2 What is the writer's opinion? Should there be a ban on adverts on television before 9pm?

3 Circle the correct words.

Should all adverts for fast food be banned?

On the one hand, everyone should be able to choose what they eat. (1) **In addition / On the other hand**, too many people have unhealthy diets. Junk food can lead to obesity. (2) **Moreover / However**, it costs the health service a lot to treat overweight people. (3) **In addition / However**, the government shouldn't have to pay for this. Another problem is that advertisers not only target adults, (4) **but they also / although they** target children. Children and adults need better education about healthy diets. I believe that companies should be allowed to advertise their products, (5) **but / nevertheless** only in certain places. (6) **Although / In addition**, companies should have to pay more tax on profits from junk food.

Writing task

Writing a for and against essay

Write a for and against essay giving your opinion about banning online advertising.

Step 1 | Plan

Complete the plan with your own ideas and opinions.

Should all online adverts be banned?			
Introduction	**On the one hand ...**	**On the other hand ...**	**Conclusion**
Nowadays, many people think ...	Online adverts are annoying ...	People should be able to advertise ...	In conclusion, I believe that ... In my opinion ...

Step 2 | Write

Write your first draft. Use your notes from Step 1 and the for and against essay on page 126 to help you.

_____
_____
_____
_____
_____
_____
_____
_____
_____
_____
_____
_____
_____

Step 3 | Check

Check your work. Check that you have:
- [ ] used connectors of addition
- [ ] used connectors of contrast
- [ ] used formal language
- [ ] organized the paragraphs correctly

Finally remember to always check your:
grammar   vocabulary   spelling

USEFUL EXPRESSIONS

Nowadays / Today, many people say / think that ...
I believe, ... / In my opinion, ... / It seems to me that ...
I am (not) in favour of ... because ...
In conclusion, ... / To sum up, ...

Step 4 | Write

Write your final copy in your notebook.

Writing hub

UNIT 9

Text type: Formal emails

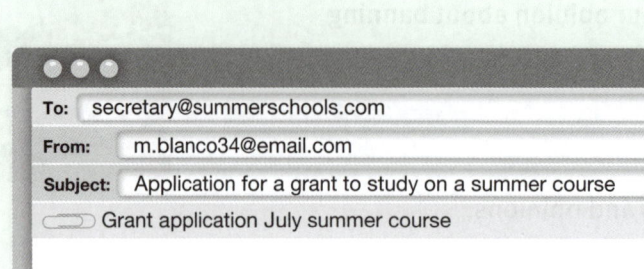

To: secretary@summerschools.com
From: m.blanco34@email.com
Subject: Application for a grant to study on a summer course
Grant application July summer course

Dear Mr Cameron,

Please find attached my completed application form for a grant for a summer course to study English in Edinburgh. As you will see, I am interested in improving my English.

I am currently a student at IES Barajas in Madrid. This year I am taking my school leaving exams in May and I am expected to pass them all with good grades. I have studied English for eight years and my level is B1. I went to a summer camp in America last year, so I already have some experience of studying abroad.

I will certainly make the most of this wonderful opportunity if I am successful in my grant application. After I leave school I hope to go to university and study languages, so I would benefit from improving my skills in English if I could do this course.

Thank you for considering my application. I look forward to hearing from you.

With best wishes,

Marta Blanco Gutiérrez

use a variety of verb tenses

use a variety of other structures eg passives, conditionals

1 Read and listen to the email. Then answer the questions. 🔊 49

1. What course is Marta applying for?
_____
2. What is she doing in May?
_____
3. How long has she studied English for?
_____
4. What did she do last summer?
_____
5. What does she hope to do after leaving school?
_____

2 Circle the correct words.

1. I am interested in **to learn / learning** more about music.
2. I look forward **to hear / to hearing** from you.
3. I hope **to become / becoming** a sports teacher.
4. I am expected **to pass / passing** all my exams.
5. I have some experience of **to live / living** abroad.
6. Thank you for **to consider / considering** my application.

3 Complete the text with the correct form of the verbs in brackets.

I (1) _____ (study) music for over ten years. Two years ago I (2) _____ (go) to a music camp in London. At the moment I (3) _____ (study) for my Grade 6 in piano. I'd love to do this course – if I (4) _____ (can) do this course it (5) _____ (help) me a lot with my studies. If you invite me to an interview, you (6) _____ (see) that I am serious about improving my skills.

Writing task

UNIT 9

Writing formal emails

Write an email to apply for a place on a summer camp. Choose from the camps in the box.

sports camp   music camp   drama camp
a camp of your own choice

Step 1 | Plan

Choose a summer camp and then complete the table with your notes.

	Your notes	Useful language
Which course have you chosen? Why are you interested in it?		As you will see, … I am particularly interested in …
What are you doing currently / this year? What previous experience have you got? When from?		I am currently … This year I am … I have studied … I am expected to …
What will happen if you get the place? How will you make the most of this opportunity?		I can assure you that … If …
How can you close the letter?		Thank you for …

Step 2 | Write

Write your first draft. Use your notes from Step 1 and the email on page 128 to help you.

_____
_____
_____
_____
_____
_____
_____
_____
_____
_____

Step 3 | Check

Check your work. Check that you have used:
- [ ] a variety of tenses
- [ ] a variety of other grammatical structures
- [ ] formal language

Finally remember to always check your:
grammar   vocabulary   spelling

USEFUL EXPRESSIONS

Please find attached my completed application form for …
Thank you for considering my application.
I look forward to hearing from you.
With best wishes,

Step 4 | Write

Write your final copy in your notebook.

External exam trainer: Reading

Your exam preparation

1 Read the information about Marta in the example task below. Which book (a, b or c) is the most suitable for Marta to read? Why?

> **Example**
> **Marta loves reading books about the past. She doesn't enjoy fiction or books about people's relationships. She doesn't have much time to read so a book that she could read from time to time would be perfect.**
>
> **a)** a romantic novel set in the Middle Ages in England
>
> **b)** a book with very short chapters about different historical periods
>
> **c)** a biography of a famous British author and poet

> ✓ **EXAM TIP:** Identify key words
>
> Look for key words in the descriptions and think about how they could be said in other ways.

ABOUT THE EXAM

Matching descriptions and texts

You are given descriptions of five different people and eight texts to match these to. There are three extra texts. This tests your ability to read multiple texts for specific information and detailed comprehension.

2 Read the descriptions of the people and underline any important information.

1 Debbie loves being active and she would like to learn a new skill, such as baking or photography. She would like a room to herself.

2 Raj wants to go to Europe as cheaply as possible. He loves sport and he's happy to work in the summer and then go travelling.

3 Kerry is in her 70s. She'd like to go somewhere where she could learn more about nature and paint or take pictures. She can't walk far and she hates cooking.

MODEL EXAM

3 Match each of the people in exercise 2 with the most suitable holiday course. Use the notes in red to help you.

A Travel to Italy and learn to photograph animals, plants and scenery. You'll learn how to take the best pictures at different times of day, as well as learning more about wildlife. You'll stay in great accommodation in Tuscany. The course lasts a week and is suitable for everyone as there is very little walking involved.

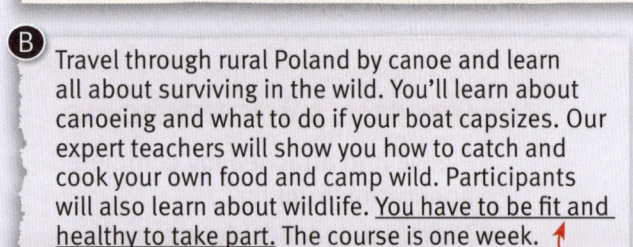

B Travel through rural Poland by canoe and learn all about surviving in the wild. You'll learn about canoeing and what to do if your boat capsizes. Our expert teachers will show you how to catch and cook your own food and camp wild. Participants will also learn about wildlife. <u>You have to be fit and healthy to take part.</u> The course is one week.

C Are you creative and do you love food? Come to France this summer! In the morning you learn about painting, pottery or photography and then in the afternoon <u>learn to prepare traditional French dishes.</u> There is time off for relaxing or, if you prefer to be more active, for walking, cycling or swimming. Accommodation is in a beautiful old farmhouse with individual rooms.

D Train to be a sports monitor for young people! On this three-day course in Spain you'll learn how to do all the different sports offered on our children's summer camps, such as canoeing, kite surfing and diving. You will receive practical training in sports tutoring and first aid. We pay for your travel and accommodation if you then work at our summer camps.

E Come and find out to make a film. These one or two-week summer courses cover different topics, such as creating storyboards, writing scripts and operating cameras. You'll also see some of the wonderful Croatian countryside and wildlife as you film on location there. <u>Accommodation is in shared rooms.</u>

Would this course be possible for someone who can't walk far?

Would this suit someone who wants to be in a room by themselves?

Would this course be suitable for someone who doesn't enjoy cooking?

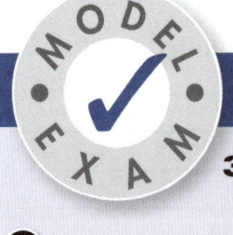

Multiple matching

Your exam practice

Step 1 — Read the descriptions.

Read the descriptions of the people and underline the key words. Think about what might be suitable for each person.

> ✓ **EXAM TIP:** Eliminate unsuitable options
>
> As you read each option, look for details that make it unsuitable. This means you can eliminate it. When you have found the option you think is correct, check all the details match.

Step 2 — Read all the options.

Read all the options carefully before you try to match them with the people.

Step 3 — Match the people and options.

Read the first description again and all the options again. Then eliminate unsuitable options, looking at the key words to help you. Decide on the best option. Then do the same for the other people.

Step 4 — Check your answer.

Read everything again and check your answers.

---

4 Read the descriptions of the people and match them with the best course for them.

1 Henry wants to do a short course to learn more about computers so he can communicate easily with his grandchildren in Australia.

2 Monica is thinking about changing to a career in performing. She loves learning new skills and dancing. She wants a course that she can do after work.

3 Jake wants a change in career, so he's looking for a short full-time course in which he can learn how to use different programs so that he can set up a business to create websites.

A Communicate
This week-long course is designed for people who use computers and cameras regularly, but who want to learn to make the most of technology to create exciting blogs and vlogs. We will look at designing a blog and easy steps to make it attractive, as well as giving tips for making vlogs and creating your own vlog channel.

B Creative computers
Learn about every aspect of designing fantastic websites, starting with the basics of good design through to creating and updating sites. You'll learn to use the most up-to-date software such as Photoshop, Dreamweaver and Flash as well as programming. This course runs for ten weeks from September to December. Basic computer skills are necessary to apply for this course.

C Performance training
Ever wanted to be in a circus? Now's your chance! Come and learn circus skills such as riding a unicycle, juggling, performing as a clown or acrobatics. This course runs every summer in France or Italy. You get to try all the different activities and then choose three to specialize in. No experience necessary.

D Technology for you
This five-day course teaches you all the basics of using a computer. You'll learn how to send emails, create and save documents, and use the internet. It also covers other aspects such as using social networking sites, buying products from online websites and connecting a computer to other equipment such as printers or scanners. No computer experience necessary.

E Lights and action!
Whether your dream is to take Hollywood by storm or have fun with a local drama group, this practical course can help. It will help to build your technical ability to perform confidently on stage and includes modules on dance and voice coaching to develop you into an all-round performer. The course runs one evening a week from September to June.

131

External exam trainer: Reading

Your exam preparation

1 Read the text in the Model exam below quickly, but not the options (A–D). Do you like K-Pop music? Which bands and singers have you heard of?

> ☑ **EXAM TIP:** Decide what kind of word is missing
>
> Read the whole text and then read each sentence again. What kind of word is missing (eg an auxiliary verb, an article, a relative pronoun, a preposition, a pronoun)?

2 Look again at the Model exam. Try to guess the words without looking at the options. Use the comments in blue to help you.

3 Do the Model exam. Were any of your ideas in exercise 2 correct?

> ☑ **EXAM TIP:** Eliminate incorrect options
>
> After reading the text, look at each gap. Read the four options and eliminate any that you are sure are incorrect. Then read the sentence again and decide which the correct answer is.

ABOUT THE EXAM

Multiple-choice cloze
You are given a text with six gaps and you choose the correct answer from four possible options. This tests your understanding of vocabulary and grammar.

4 Read the text below and choose the correct word (A, B, C or D) for each space.

K-Pop

Over the last 10 to 15 years, Korean pop music, known as 'K-Pop' has become popular all (1) _____ the world. This music is typically fun and catchy and also very visual: every K-Pop song has its own complicated dance routine and the young boy and girl singers in K-Pop bands are usually talented (2) _____ and acrobats as well as singers. The K-Pop record companies hold special (3) _____ to discover new stars. The winners, who are usually very young, often between 10 and 12 years old, then spend years training in special schools. At the end of this process, only a small number of the best performers will be invited to join a group and even (4) _____ will be chosen to become solo artists.

Look at the words before and after the gap and use your knowledge of words that often go together in English – all over the world and all around the world are common set expressions.

Look for clues earlier in the sentence. The mention of dance routines helps us to know that the right answer here must be dancers.

The missing words will be ones which you've studied before. They're common ones for the level (B1).

Use your knowledge of grammar – we can see that the missing word is a comparative adjective that talks about quantity. Performers is a countable noun, so we know that the answer must be few/fewer (not less/lesser which refer to uncountable nouns).

1 A over   B in   C about   D inside
2 A artists   B dancers   C players   D actors
3 A lessons   B exams   C competitions D testing
4 A smaller   B fewer   C lesser   D few

132

Multiple-choice cloze

Your exam practice

Step 1 Get an overview.

Read the text in Your exam below.

Step 2 Read the text and guess the words.

Read the text again and see if you can fill any of the gaps without looking at the options. Then read the options and see if any of your answers appear there.

Step 3 Choose the correct option.

Think about the options A–D and decide which one is the best answer. Think about why the answer you chose is correct and why the other answers are incorrect.

Step 4 Read again.

Once all the gaps are completed, read the whole text again with your answers to make sure it makes sense.

---

5 Read the text below and choose the correct word (A, B, C or D) for each space.

For the love of music

Lori Park is a 16-year-student in New York with an unusual part-time job. He is part of a group that (1) _____ videos for the K-Pop girl band *Red Velvet*. There are hundreds of thousands of K-Pop fans in America, but although their songs are often – but not (2) _____ – in English, the shows, TV and radio interviews and other special events are usually in (3) _____. Lori is a native Korean speaker – his mother is American but his father is from Korea – and he is a big fan of K-pop. So, together with some other Korean-speaking *Red Velvet* fans, he decided to start translating videos of his favourite band into English so that international fans would be able to (4) _____ them. Lori produces English subtitles for videos online and he also translates the band's (5) _____ media pages, fan website and official announcements about new songs and tours. He and his friends don't earn any money for this: they do it all for free. Lori says he is (6) _____ by his love for the music and the knowledge that what he does will help to share that music with others around the world.

1. A watches B makes C translates D records
2. A never B always C sometimes D rarely
3. A Korea B America C English D Korean
4. A understanding B understood C understand D have understood
5. A internet B video C music D social
6. A motivated B interested C excited D decided

External exam trainer: Reading

Your exam preparation

1 Read the text in the Model exam below. Which of the cultures described sounds most similar to yours?

> ✓ **EXAM TIP:** Read each line carefully
> Always read the text all the way through first. Make sure you look carefully at the words before and after the gaps before you write your answers.

2 Read the text again and the comments in red. Think about what type of word is missing in each gap. Is it a(n):
- verb?
- pronoun?
- preposition?
- adverb?

ABOUT THE EXAM

Open cloze
You are given a text with six gaps and you have to write the missing word. There are no multiple choice options in this part. You can only write one word per gap. This exam tests your comprehension skills and your ability to complete a text using appropriate vocabulary and grammar.

> ✓ **EXAM TIP:** Don't leave anything blank
> If you have read the sentence several times and still do not know the answer, guess. Do not leave any gaps unanswered.

3 Complete the gaps in the Model exam with the correct words.

MODEL EXAM

4 For these questions, write the correct answer in each gap.

I've just come back from a year abroad on an exchange programme in Finland. I'm (1) _____ Mexico and I studied at an art and design school in Helsinki. It was a great place and I had a fantastic time there, but I (2) _____ expected that Finnish culture would be so different from Mexican culture. Finnish people are actually very friendly but they smile less than Mexicans. Mexicans smile more, talk more and they talk very (3) _____. I couldn't believe how slowly and quietly my Finnish friends spoke. The slowness made me impatient at first, but now I like it. In Mexico, when young people meet each other, we kiss on both cheeks, but in Finland, people usually (4) _____ hands. My Finnish friends were very surprised when I kissed them!

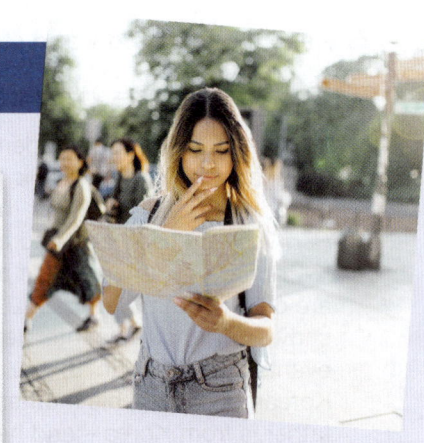

(1) This word describes the position of something.

(2) This word describes an action.

(3) This word comes directly before a verb.

(4) This is an 'action word' that comes after the subject of the sentence.

Open cloze

Your exam practice

Step 1 Get an overview.

5 Read the text in Your exam below. Do you agree with the author's opinion?

Step 2 Analyse the gaps.

Read the text again and look at the words before and after each gap. Think about the function of the words and decide what type of word is missing in each space.

Step 3 Complete the gaps.

Complete the gaps with your answers.

Step 4 Read again.

Once all the gaps are completed, read the whole text again. Make sure each answer makes sense in the sentence and in the whole text.

✓ **EXAM TIP:** Spelling

Remember to check your spelling. You must spell the words correctly or you will lose marks!

6 For these questions, write the correct answer in each gap.

You only have one opportunity to make a good first impression at a job interview – and you have less (1) _____ one minute to do it! Scientists have discovered that when people meet a new person for the first time, they form an opinion about him or (2) _____ in the first 30 seconds. And this opinion is based entirely on what the person (3) _____ like, not what they say or do. So this is why it is so important to pay attention to (4) _____ appearance. You should (5) _____ wear jeans and a T-shirt, for example. Even if they are smart and fashionable: you should always make the effort to be more formally dressed. Smart clothes and a smile are essential. And, speaking of a smile, don't forget to brush your teeth. Scientists also found that the positive impression produced by a smile can (6) _____ into a negative one if the person has bad teeth!

External exam trainer: Listening

Your exam preparation

1 Read the questions in the Model exam. Match questions 1 and 2 with topics a–d.

   a) camping
   b) sport
   c) nature and countryside
   d) mountain climbing

> ✓ **EXAM TIP: Predict**
> Look at the pictures carefully and predict the words you will hear.

2 Look at the pictures in the Model exam. Which set of words do you think you might hear for each question? Listen and check. 🔊 50

   a) stove / tent / sleeping bag
   b) rope / boots / helmet

> ✓ **EXAM TIP: Justify your answers**
> Sometimes the answer choices include distractors. They might contain the same words that you hear in the listening exam, but this doesn't necessarily mean that they are the correct answers! Make sure you can always justify your answers.

ABOUT THE EXAM
Multiple-choice pictures
You will listen to seven short recordings you must match to the correct picture. This tests your ability to listen for key information.

3 Listen again and choose the correct picture in the Model exam.

4 Now look at Your exam on page 137. Follow steps 1–4. 🔊 51

Step 1	Read all the questions.
Step 2	Look at all the pictures.
Step 3	Listen carefully. Choose the correct answers.
Step 4	Listen again and check your answers.

MODEL EXAM

Listen to two short extracts. Choose the correct picture.

1 What problem did Chris have when he went camping?

   A   B   C

2 What does Maria need to bring for her mountain climbing course?

   A   B   C

Multiple-choice pictures

Your exam practice

1. Where is Katie now?

   A  / B  / C

2. Who is Josh going to work with when he does his work experience?

   A  / B  / C

3. What sort of holiday did Caroline have?

   A  / B  / C

4. When is Ben going to the doctor's?

   A  / B  / C

5. Which bag is Liz going to buy?

   A  / B  / C

External exam trainer: Listening

Your exam preparation

1 Read the example exam task and possible answers. Answer the questions.

1. How many people are there in the conversation?
2. Is the question asking about an attitude or an opinion?

> **Example**
> You will hear two friends talking about a new football stadium which has just been built in their town. They agree that …
>
> a) The town needs better public services, not a football stadium.
> b) Football brings people together.
> c) Building the stadium was a waste of money.

☑ **EXAM TIP:** Read before you listen

Before you listen, look at the questions and carefully read the three options. Focus on the key words in each option and how these differ from one another.

ABOUT THE EXAM

Multiple choice answers
You will listen to six short conversations and choose the correct answer for each one. There are three options for each question. This tests your ability to understand people's attitudes or opinions and to listen for key information.

2 Read and listen to the Model exam below. Are all the options (a–c) mentioned in the conversation? 🔊 52

3 Look at the conversation in the Model exam again. Match sentences 1–3 with options a–c in exercise 1.

☑ **EXAM TIP:** Using synoyms

Remember that you might also hear synonyms of the key words. Before you listen think about possible synonyms for the key words.

4 Look at the example question in exercise 1 again. Which answer is correct in the Model exam, a), b) or c)? Which phrase has got a similar meaning to 'I agree with you'?

MODEL EXAM

Marion: Have you seen they've just finished building the new football stadium at last? It's enormous!

Bob: ¹ Yes, it's ridiculously big. What a waste of money!

Marion: Why is it a waste of money? I know you're not interested in football but lots of people are and ² watching a match creates great community spirit.

Bob: OK, so some people like going to football matches but I think the money the town spent on the stadium could have been used in other ways ³ to pay for more important things – better roads, a new hospital, improved services for old people, for example.

Marion: I see what you mean about that, but in fact I think most of the money for the stadium came from a private company: the town didn't actually pay for it. And none of the things you mentioned are as exciting as having a big new stadium and the Rangers winning their next match!

Multiple-choice (gist)

Your exam practice

Step 1 — Understand the situation.

Read the instructions and make sure you understand what you have to do.

Step 2 — Read the questions and answer options.

Look at the questions and options and think about who the speakers are and what type of information you need to listen for.

Step 3 — Listen and choose the correct answers.

Listen carefully to the attitude and opinions of the speakers. Choose the option which you think best matches the main message of what they say.

Step 4 — Listen again and check your answers.

You will hear the recording again directly after the first time. Listen again and make sure you are happy with your answers.

YOUR EXAM

5 Listen to six short conversations. For each question choose the correct answer a), b) or c). You will hear the conversations twice. 🔊 53

1. You will hear two friends talking about a job interview. Why does Megan believe that Jo has a good chance of success?
   a) Because Jo has the best skills and qualifications.
   b) Because a small accident doesn't matter if you are the right person for the job.
   c) Because she knows that Jo gave good answers to the interviewers' questions.

2. You will hear a brother and sister talking about a family argument. How does the boy feel about it?
   a) He is upset.
   b) He isn't worried about it.
   c) He is surprised.

3. You will hear two friends talking about cooking. What does Karen think about Mike's way of cooking potatoes?
   a) It's unhealthy and Karen would never cook them the same way.
   b) Mike uses too much salt and bad quality oil.
   c) The potatoes are very salty but they taste extremely good.

4. You will hear two friends talking about a concert. Why was Jane disappointed?
   a) Because the singer didn't dance on stage.
   b) Because the concert was too short.
   c) Because the singer didn't give a good performance.

5. You will hear two schoolfriends talking about a party. What's Deb's real reason for not going to it?
   a) She's angry with Lisa.
   b) She promised to spend time with her cousins.
   c) She doesn't want to upset Lisa.

6. You will hear a mother and son talking about a new phone. They agree that…
   a) modern phones have become too complicated.
   b) we're used to having phones that can do lots of things.
   c) phones are getting easier to use.

External exam trainer: Listening

Your exam preparation

1 Read the notes about The World Heritage Site Programme. Answer the questions.

1. Why was it started?
2. What types of things can become World Heritage sites?

> ✓ **EXAM TIP:** Think about what you already know
>
> Think about the knowledge you already have about this subject. What you know can give you a context and help you answer the questions.

ABOUT THE EXAM

Completing notes
You will hear a monologue or a dialogue. You must complete six gaps in the notes with words or numbers. This tests your ability to listen for specific information.

2 Look at gaps 1–6 in the Model exam. What kind of information will you need? Match a–f with gaps 1–6.

a) a year
b) an adjective
c) a country
d) a region or city
e) a number
f) a name of an organization

> ✓ **EXAM TIP:** Analyse the missing information
>
> Look at the gaps in the notes and try to work out what kind of word or number you need. Will you need a verb, a noun or an adjective? Will it be a price, a year or a time?

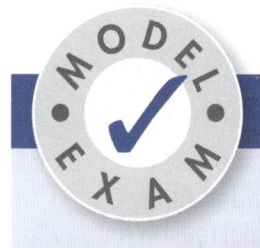

MODEL EXAM

3 Listen to the information and complete the gaps. You will hear the information twice. 🔊 54

The World Heritage Site Programme

☞ the programme was founded by (1) …
☞ it was started in (2) …
☞ A World Heritage Site can be:
  • a place of great natural beauty, eg an area of mountains, forest, lakes, desert, etc.
  • a building or man-made environment which is important for cultural, historical or (3) … reasons.
☞ first World Heritage Site was in the (4) … in Egypt.
☞ there are now (5) … World Heritage Sites.
☞ (6) … has the most sites with 53 followed by China with 52.

Completing notes

Your exam practice

Step 1 — Read the instructions carefully.

4 Read the instructions in Your exam and answer the questions.
1. What is the programme about?
2. How many times will you hear the information?
3. How many gaps are there?

Step 2 — Read all the notes.

5 Read the notes in Your exam. Which one of these things is *not* mentioned?
1. how many people live in the city
2. where the city is
3. things to do in the city
4. how to get around in the city
5. parks and green spaces in the city

Step 3 — Analyse the gaps.

6 Study gaps 1–6 in Your exam. What kind of answers do you think you will need? Choose a), b) or c).

1. a) an adjective   b) an adverb   c) a verb
2. a) a country   b) a city   c) a type of landscape
3. a) a noun   b) a verb   c) an adjective
4. a) an adjective   b) a number   c) a date
5. a) a type of vehicle   b) type of business   c) type of job
6. a) a large number b) a date   c) a small number

Step 4 — Listen carefully and write the answers.

Step 5 — Listen again and check your answers.

YOUR EXAM

7 You are going to hear part of the programme about the ultra-modern city of Songdo in South Korea. Listen and complete the notes. You will hear the information twice. 🔊 55

Songdo
Songdo a new, still unfinished, technological city.
Built on land that used to be (1) …

Location
Songdo is near (2) …

Facilities
Heat, lighting, rubbish, (3) … systems and transport all digitally controlled.
Big parks in city centre, (4) … per cent green space.
Transport: electric underground railway or (5) …

City life
Quiet, safe and healthy: good air quality; not crowded – the population is (6) …

External exam trainer: Listening

Your exam preparation

1 Read the instructions and example sentences. What are you going to hear?

Instructions
Listen to Alex talking about a film he watched recently. Decide if the example sentences are true or false.

Examples
1 The film has just come out.   YES / NO
2 The film is set in the eighties.   YES / NO

2 Copy the example sentences from exercise 1 into your notebook. Then translate them into your language.

3 Underline the key words in the example sentences.

ABOUT THE EXAM

Yes / No activity
You will hear a monologue or dialogue. You have to decide if six sentences are correct or incorrect. This tests your ability to understand a conversation and listen for key information.

✓ EXAM TIP: Don't panic!

If there is a word or sentence that you don't understand, don't panic! Try to focus on the next section and remember that you will hear the recording twice.

4 Read the instructions in exercise 1 again and answer the questions.
   1 Are you going to hear a monologue or a dialogue?
   2 Who is talking?
   3 What is he talking about?

5 Read and listen. Are the example sentences in exercise 1 true or false? 🔊 56

MODEL EXAM

BLADERUNNER is a science-fiction film which stars actor Harrison Ford. It's not a recent film – it first came out in 1982 – but it's very exciting and the acting is fantastic. The story takes place in the future in Los Angeles in the USA – which has become a city full of high-rise buildings and flying vehicles. The technology for building robots has become very advanced and now there are some robots which are so much like human beings that people don't know the difference. The main character is a police detective called Rick Deckard, played by Harrison Ford. His job is to find and catch some of these dangerous human robots who are also chasing him at the same time. It's a very unusual story and a film I could watch again and again.

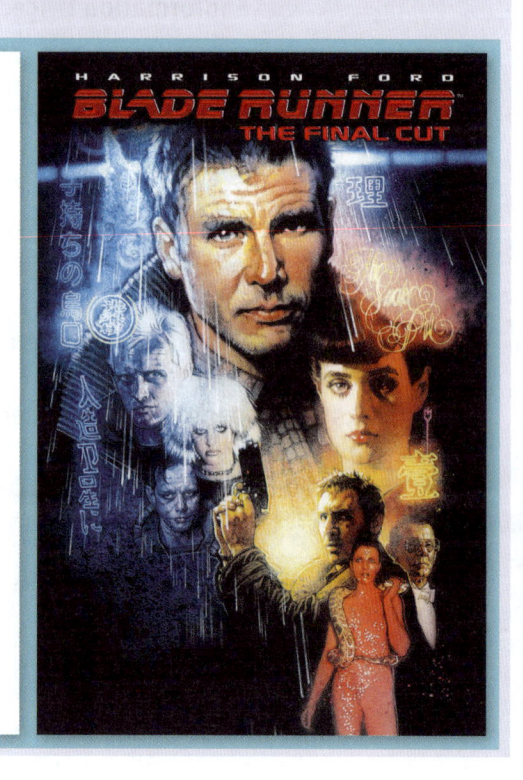

Yes / No activity

Your exam practice

Step 1 — Read the instructions.

6 Read the instructions in Your exam. Then answer the questions.

1. Are you going to hear a monologue or a dialogue?
2. Who is talking?
3. What are they talking about?

> ✓ **EXAM TIP: Key words**
>
> When you read the questions, underline the key words (= the important words), eg words like nouns, adjectives and verbs. This helps you know what to listen for.

Step 2 — Read all the sentences.

7 Copy sentences 1–6 from Your exam into your notebook. Translate them into your language.

Step 3 — Think about the key words.

Underline the key words in sentences 1–6. If necessary, check their meaning in a dictionary.

Step 4 — Listen and choose the correct answers.

Step 5 — Listen again and check your answers.

YOUR EXAM

8 Listen to a conversation between Olivia and Greg about language learning. Decide if each sentence is correct or incorrect. 🔊 57

1 Knowing a certain language can help you learn another one.	YES / NO
2 An Arabic speaker would probably find Farsi more difficult than an English speaker.	YES / NO
3 English, German and Farsi are closely related to each other.	YES / NO
4 One of the factors that make a language difficult is its grammar.	YES / NO
5 It's easy to speak Mandarin because the grammar isn't complicated.	YES / NO
6 Speaking Mandarin is more difficult than writing it.	YES / NO

External exam trainer: Writing

Your exam preparation

1 Read the instructions in the example task below and answer the questions.

1. Who must the writer write to and why?
2. What kind of text is it? Is this a formal or an informal situation?
3. What must the writer include in the email?
4. How many words must the writer write?

> **Example**
> You are applying for a summer job in a vet's surgery to help with looking after the animals. In the application you have to include a short description of yourself. In your description you should say:
> - what you are studying at school or what you are doing at the moment
> - what work experience you have that is relevant to the job
> - your personal skills and why you would be good at the job

2 Read the task again and Jake's answer in the Model exam. Does Jake include all of the information in the exam task?

ABOUT THE EXAM

An email
You write an email of around 100 words in response to some prompts, eg a written note, an advert, etc. This tests your ability to follow instructions and communicate clearly and effectively.

☑ **EXAM TIP:** Understand *who* the message is for and *why* you're writing

Read the task and check you understand who the message is for and the purpose of the message. This will help you decide if you need to use formal or informal language and what you need to communicate in your text.

3 Read Jake's answer in the Model exam again. Find one example of …

1. an extra piece of information not asked for in the notes.
   _____
2. a question asking for information.
   _____

4 Read Jake's email applying for a summer job with a vet and write your own application. Include the same information about you. Write about 100 words.

From	jsloane@email.com
To	simonvet@email.com
Subject	Summer job

Dear Sir/Madam,

I am writing to apply for the job advertised in the Town News to work in your vet's surgery.

I am currently in Year 11 and will be taking my GCSE exams in May. I love cats. Last summer I pet-sat for my neighbours for a month. This included feeding the animals and walking the dogs regularly. I am responsible and organized and I work well in a team. I have good communication skills and I have some experience of looking after animals which I am sure would help in this job. I enjoy learning and I'm sure this would be a great opportunity to learn more about taking care of animals. Could you please let me know what the starting date is?

I look forward to hearing from you,

Yours faithfully,

Jake Simons

An email

Your exam practice

Step 1 Read the descriptions.

Read the exam task in Your exam below. Answer questions 1–4 in exercise 1 from Your exam preparation.

Step 2 Plan your email.

Decide how to respond to the prompts and what extra information you want to include and write notes.

Step 3 Write your email.

Make sure you include responses to all the prompts in the exam task. Remember to write enough words!

Step 4 Check your email.

When you finish, take time to read your email carefully several times and check your spelling and grammar.

☑ **EXAM TIP:** Use a variety of grammatical structures

In a writing exam, you must show the examiner that you can use a variety of grammatical structures. Make sure you use different verb tenses and try to include at least one example of a present, past and future tense.

YOUR EXAM

5 You are applying for a grant to study English for a year in New York. You are writing to Mrs Baxter at m.baxterapulse@email.com and you are attaching your CV. Include this information.

- why you are writing / what you are applying for
- what you are studying at the moment
- why you want to study in New York
- what language and personal skills you have

EXAM KIT: USEFUL LANGUAGE

Greeting	• Dear Mr/Ms		
Opening line	• I am writing to	• I am contacting you because	
Referring to attachments	• Please find attached	• I attach	• As you will see
Ending	• I look forward to hearing from you	• Yours sincerely	• Yours faithfully

External exam trainer: Writing

Your exam preparation

1 Read the instructions in the Model exam below. How many texts do you have to write?

2 Read the tasks and answers for both questions 1 and 2 in the Model exam. Which task would you prefer to do? Why?

3 Read the instructions, task and answer in question 1 again. Check that the writer has answered all the questions.

✓ EXAM TIP: Writing

1 Write a beginning, a middle and an end.
2 Make sure you respond to all the questions and prompts.
3 Use words and phrases to explain the order of events.
4 Use a variety of expressions and vocabulary.
5 Use adjectives and adverbs to describe how people are feeling.
6 Remember to include your own thoughts and opinions.

ABOUT THE EXAM

An article or a story
You can choose whether to write an article or a story.
For the article you are given some notes which you should read carefully. The language you use is typically more informal and conversational; for example, you should ask the reader some direct questions.
For the story, you are usually given the first line or sometimes just the context and asked to develop the story from there.
These test your flexibility in using a variety of grammatical structures and verb tenses as well as your ability to use a wide range of vocabulary and different linking words to join ideas together.

4 Now read the answer in question 2. Which words in the Exam kit on page 147 has the writer used?

5 Read the Exam tips. Which are more useful for writing an article? Which are more useful for a story? Which could be both?

MODEL EXAM

Write an answer to one of the two questions below. Write about 100 words.

Tell us about a personal challenge you'd like to try:
What is it?   What do you hope to get from doing it?
Why have you decided to do it?   What do you think you will find most difficult?

Question 1 Write an article about a personal challenge you'd like to try.
Question 2 Write a story. Begin with this first line: *'Oh no!' I thought, 'What shall I do?'*

My technology-free challenge

I would like to challenge myself to spend a year living without technology. Why do I want to do this? Because I've realized that I am spending all my time indoors in front of my computer or on my phone, and I want to spend more time in nature. It will be difficult at first: the worst thing will be not having a phone to speak to my friends as soon as I want to. But, on the other hand, when I do speak to them, perhaps I will value it more. The best thing will be having more time and I hope to become calmer and happier from not checking my phone and social media all the time!

'Oh no!' I thought, 'What shall I do?' The race that I had trained for all year was about to start. The other runners were already getting into their starting positions on the running track, but I had arrived at the athletics club only three minutes earlier. I rushed down to the field at the speed of lightning, got out my running kit to change and discovered, to my horror, that I'd forgotten my shoes! But then suddenly I knew what to do. The grass felt warm and soft under my bare feet as I walked down to my starting position. Some of the best runners in the world run without shoes.

An article or a story

Your exam practice

6 Read the exam task in Your exam below and choose one of the tasks.

An article

Step 1 Read the instructions.

Underline any important information or questions you need to respond to.

Step 2 Plan your article.

Decide on the subject and content of your article. Try to use your own experience and knowledge.

Step 3 Write your article.

Remember to respond to all the questions or prompts.

Step 4 Check your spelling and grammar.

> **EXAM TIP:** Make notes
> Before you start writing your answer, write notes for each point and then organize the notes in a logical order.

A story

Step 1 Read the instructions.

Read the instructions and the title or opening sentence.

Step 2 Plan your story.

Think of a beginning, middle and end.

Step 3 Write your story.

Remember to use words and phrases to organize your story.

Step 4 Check your spelling and grammar.

Your Exam

7 Write an answer to one of the two questions below. Write about 100 words.

Question 1 You see this advert on a website. Write an article responding to the advert:

> *Tell us about a film, play or concert you have been to or a book you have read.*
> What is the title of the film/book, etc? Why did you choose to see/read it? Who wrote/sang/acted, etc in it?
> Write an article answering these questions and we will read out the best ones on our weekly radio programme.

Question 2 Your English teacher has asked you to write a story for homework. You must begin with this line:

Slowly and carefully I opened the door.

EXAM KIT: USEFUL LANGUAGE

Linkers and connectors

An article
- so
- as well
- though
- in addition
- although
- however

A story
- At first
- suddenly
- later
- finally
- on the other hand
- then
- after
- next
- in the end

Useful expressions
- I was (walking home) when I (found) …
- never … before
- If I hadn't found it, I would …
- I wish …
- What do you think I should do? / What would you do if you were me?

Phrase book

Functional language

Starter unit   Phrases for a presentation
Good morning / afternoon!
Today I'm going to talk about …
First of all, I'm going to show you …
After that, feel free to ask me any questions.
These are some of the fun things I did …
In this photo you can see …

Unit 1   Talking about skills and interests
I'm good at … and …
I'm really interested in …
I've had some experience of …
For example, …
People often say that I'm …
What I find most exciting about this opportunity is …

Unit 2   Using question tags
That's the most important thing, **isn't it**?
That isn't very useful, **is it**?
It'll be boiling hot, **won't it**?
I don't think we'll need it, **will we**?
We could use that for (cooking), **couldn't we**?
We wouldn't use that, **would we**?

Unit 3   Phrases for interviews
Pleased to meet you.
Please take a seat.
Thanks for coming in today.
We'll let you know our decision …
I look forward to hearing from you.
It's been a pleasure to meet you.

Unit 4   Presenting your opinion
Personally, I'd say that …
I think / don't think that …
In my view, …
If you ask me, …
In my opinion, …
For me, …

Unit 5   Sequencing events
In the early / mid- / late (1990s), …
Then / Next / After that, …
The following year, …
Later / (A few) years later, …
It wasn't until (1985) that …
By (2020), …

Unit 6   Giving counter-arguments
I don't see it like that at all.
I'm afraid I don't agree.
I'm sorry, but I completely disagree.
That's not how I see it.
You've made some interesting points, but I see things differently.

Unit 7   Phrases for surveys
I'm doing some research into …
Could I ask you a few questions?
It won't take more than five minutes.
I'll be taking notes – is that OK?
OK, let's get started!
Would you mind me telling me … ?
Is there anything else you'd like to add?

Unit 8   Phrases for persuading
We're sure you'll agree that …
Don't they look … ?
You really should / ought to …
Go on – treat yourself!
We guarantee that …
Please …

Unit 9   Expressing opinions
In my opinion, …
It's an interesting point, but …
That's not really true, is it?
Another argument is that …
I'm sorry, but I completely disagree.

Pronunciation reference

Phonemes

Vowel sounds			Consonants		
short vowels	long vowels	diphthongs	voiced ↔ unvoiced		
/æ/ cat	/ɑː/ park	/eə/ hair	/b/ ball	/p/ pen	/m/ man
/e/ bed	/ɜː/ girl	/ɪə/ year	/d/ day	/t/ time	/n/ now
/ɪ/ it	/ɔː/ door	/ʊə/ tour	/g/ good	/k/ computer	/ŋ/ thing
/ɒ/ hot	/iː/ see	/aɪ/ buy	/v/ have	/f/ five	/h/ house
/ʊ/ good	/uː/ food	/eɪ/ game	/z/ zoo	/s/ say	/l/ look
/ʌ/ cup		/ɔɪ/ boy	/ʒ/ vision	/ʃ/ shy	/r/ relax
/ə/ number		/əʊ/ go	/ð/ brother	/θ/ think	/w/ website
		/aʊ/ house	/dʒ/ jeans	/tʃ/ teacher	/j/ yellow

Word stress

The way you pronounce different syllables is not the same in all English words. Only one syllable has the main stress. The other syllables in the word are very weakly stressed and are often pronounced using a weak schwa /ə/ sound.

/ˈlaɪbrəri/
library
● • •

/ˈɪntrəstɪŋ/
interesting
● • •

/ˈtiːtʃə(r)/
teacher
● •

/ˈbrʌðə(r)/
brother
● •

Word stress can change within the same word family when the number of syllables changes.

photograph → *photographer*
● • •   • ● • •

Intonation

Intonation is the music of the language: it is the way the voice rises and falls when we speak. When we ask *wh-* questions, the intonation usually goes down at the end. In polite questions, it usually rises at the end.

What activities do you usually do?

Can you tell me how to get to the airport?

Wordlist

A

ability (n) /əˈbɪləti/
absolutely (adv) /ˌæbsəˈluːtli/
accessories (jewellery, handbags, etc.) (n pl) /əkˈsesəriz/
accommodation (n) /əˌkɒməˈdeɪʃ(ə)n/
active listening (n) /ˌæktɪv ˈlɪs(ə)nɪŋ/
activist (n) /ˈæktɪvɪst/
ad agency (n) /ˈæd ˌeɪdʒənsi/
admit (v) /ədˈmɪt/
advantage (n) /ədˈvɑːntɪdʒ/
advert (n) /ˈædvɜː(r)t/
advertising campaign (n) /ˈædvə(r)taɪzɪŋ kæmˌpeɪn/
advertising takeover (n) /ˈædvə(r)taɪzɪŋ ˌteɪkəʊvə(r)/
agree (v) /əˈɡriː/
airbrush (v) /ˈeə(r)ˌbrʌʃ/
aircraft simulator (n) /ˈeə(r) krɑːft ˌsɪmjʊˈleɪtə(r)/
a.k.a. (also known as) /ˌeɪ keɪ ˈeɪ/
alert (v) /əˈlɜː(r)t/
always (adv) /ˈɔːlweɪz/
ambassador (n) /æmˈbæsədə(r)/
ancient (adj) /ˈeɪnʃ(ə)nt/
angry (adj) /ˈæŋɡri/
app (n) /æp/
appearance (n) /əˈpɪərəns/
application (n) /ˌæplɪˈkeɪʃ(ə)n/
apply for a job /əˌplaɪ fər ə ˈdʒɒb/
apprentice (n) /əˈprentɪs/
apprenticeship (n) /əˈprentɪsʃɪp/
ask (v) /ɑːsk/
ask (someone) out (phr vb) /ˌɑːsk (sʌmwʌn) ˈaʊt/
assertiveness (n) /əˈsɜː(r)tɪvnəs/
assessment (exams are a type of assessment) (n) /əˈsesmənt/
asset (n) /ˈæset/
assist (v) /əˈsɪst/
assistant (n) /əˈsɪstənt/
audience (n) /ˈɔːdiəns/
avalanche (n) /ˈævəˌlɑːnʧ/
award (n) /əˈwɔː(r)d/
awareness (n) /əˈweə(r)nəs/

B

bake cupcakes /ˌbeɪk ˈkʌpkeɪks/
ban (v) /bæn/
bandage (v) /ˈbændɪdʒ/
bank account (n) /ˈbæŋk əˌkaʊnt/
bargain (n) /ˈbɑː(r)ɡɪn/
be in a coma /ˌbiː ɪn ə ˈkəʊmə/
be integrated into /ˌbiː ˈɪntɪɡreɪtɪd ɪntuː/
be stuck /ˌbi ˈstʌk/
beliefs (n pl) /bɪˈliːfs/
biased (adj) /ˈbaɪəst/
billboard (n) /ˈbɪlˌbɔː(r)d/
bioplastics (n pl) /ˌbaɪəʊˈplæstɪks/
bite (v) /baɪt/
blade (n) /bleɪd/
bleed (v) /bliːd/
blister (n) /ˈblɪstə(r)/
body language (n) /ˈbɒdi ˌlæŋɡwɪdʒ/
boiling (adj) /ˈbɔɪlɪŋ/
bolt (lightning bolt) (n) /bəʊlt/
bombard (v) /bɒmˈbɑː(r)d/
boost (v) /buːst/
borrow (v) /ˈbɒrəʊ/
bother (v) /ˈbɒðə/
brand (n) /brænd/
breaking news (n) /ˌbreɪkɪŋ ˈnjuːz/
bring up (phr vb) /ˌbrɪŋ ˈʌp/
broadcast (v) /ˈbrɔːdˌkɑːst/
broadsheet (n) /ˈbrɔːdˌʃiːt/
browser (n) /ˈbraʊzə(r)/
budget (v) /ˈbʌdʒɪt/
buff (an expert) (n) /bʌf/
burn (v) /bɜː(r)n/

C

cab (n) /kæb/
camera operator (n) /ˈkæm(ə)rə ˌɒpəreɪtə(r)/
campaign (n) /kæmˈpeɪn/
campsite (n) /ˈkæmpˌsaɪt/
cancel (v) /ˈkæns(ə)l/
capsize (v) /ˌkæpˈsaɪz/
captive audience (n) /ˌkæptɪv ˈɔːdiəns/
card trick (n) /ˈkɑː(r)d ˌtrɪk/
cast (of a play/film) (n) /kɑːst/
casualties (n pl) /ˈkæʒuəltiz/
catch fire /ˌkætʃ ˈfaɪə(r)/
catchy (adj) /ˈkætʃi/
cat-crazy (adj) /ˈkætˌkreɪzi/
cat-themed (adj) /ˈkætˌθiːmd/
celebrity (n) /səˈlebrəti/
challenge (n) /ˈtʃælɪndʒ/
channel (v) /ˈtʃæn(ə)l/
channel (on TV) (n) /ˈtʃæn(ə)l/
charity (n) /ˈtʃærəti/
cheat (v) /tʃiːt/
check out (phr vb) /ˌtʃek ˈaʊt/
childhood obesity (n) /ˌtʃaɪldhʊd əʊˈbiːsəti/
choke (v) /tʃəʊk/
circulation (n) /ˌsɜː(r)kjʊˈleɪʃ(ə)n/
citizenship (n) /ˈsɪtɪz(ə)nʃɪp/
clean a wound /ˌkliːn ə ˈwuːnd/
clever (adj) /ˈklevə(r)/
coach sports /ˌkəʊtʃ ˈspɔː(r)ts/
code (n) /kəʊd/
coder (computer coder) (n) /ˈkəʊdə(r)/
collaboration (n) /kəˌlæbəˈreɪʃ(ə)n/
collapse (v) /kəˈlæps/
come across (phr vb) /ˌkʌm əˈkrɒs/
comfortable (adj) /ˈkʌmftəb(ə)l/
comfortably (adv) /ˈkʌmftəbli/
committed to /kəˈmɪtɪd ˌtuː/

communicator (n) /kəˌmjuːnɪˈkeɪtə(r)/
compensation (money you get if there is a problem) (n) /ˌkɒmpenˈseɪʃ(ə)n/
complain (v) /kəmˈpleɪn/
conflict resolution (n) /ˈkɒnflɪkt rezəˌluːʃ(ə)n/
connect (with) (v) /kəˈnekt (wɪð)/
console (n) /ˈkɒnsəʊl/
consumer (n) /kənˈsjuːmə(r)/
convince (v) /kənˈvɪns/
cookie (n) /ˈkʊki/
cooperation (n) /kəʊˌɒpəˈreɪʃ(ə)n/
copy-cat campaign (n) /ˈkɒpikæt kæmˌpeɪn/
costume designer (n) /ˈkɒstjuːm dɪˌzaɪnə(r)/
couch potato (n) /ˌkaʊtʃ pəˈteɪtəʊ/
counsellor (n) /ˈkaʊns(ə)lə(r)/
course (n) /kɔː(r)s/
coursework (n) /ˈkɔː(r)sˌwɜː(r)k/
crash (v) /kræʃ/
creative thinking (n) /kriˌeɪtɪv ˈθɪŋkɪŋ/
credit card (n) /ˈkredɪt ˌkɑː(r)d/
credit rating (n) /ˈkredɪt ˌreɪtɪŋ/
credits (at end of film/TV programme) (n pl) /ˈkredɪts/
crew (a film crew) (n) /kruː/
crowded (adj) /ˈkraʊdɪd/
crowd-funding (n) /ˈkraʊdˌfʌndɪŋ/

D

damage (v) /ˈdæmɪdʒ/
dance (n) /dɑːns/
dancer (n) /ˈdɑːnsə(r)/
dangerous (adj) /ˈdeɪndʒərəs/
database (n) /ˈdeɪtəˌbeɪs/
deadline (n) /ˈdedˌlaɪn/
debit card (n) /ˈdebɪt ˌkɑː(r)d/
debt (amount of money you owe) (n) /det/
dedicate (v) /ˈdedɪkeɪt/
delete (v) /dɪˈliːt/
delighted (adj) /dɪˈlaɪtɪd/
deposit (money in an account) (v) /dɪˈpɒzɪt/
desalinated water (n) /diːˌsælɪneɪtɪd ˈwɔːtə(r)/
design a prototype /dɪˌzaɪn ə ˈprəʊtətaɪp/
design a website /dɪˌzaɪn ə ˈwebsaɪt/
designer (n) /dɪˈzaɪnə(r)/
desperate measures (n pl) /ˌdesp(ə)rət ˈmeʒə(r)z/
destination (n) /ˌdestɪˈneɪʃ(ə)n/
devastated (adj) /ˈdevəˌsteɪtɪd/
develop an idea /dɪˌveləp ən aɪˈdɪə/
dilemma (n) /dɪˈlemə/
dirty (adj) /ˈdɜː(r)ti/
disability (n) /ˌdɪsəˈbɪləti/
disable (cookies) (v) /dɪsˈeɪb(ə)l/
disadvantage (n) /ˌdɪsədˈvɑːntɪdʒ/
disaster (n) /dɪzˈɑːstə(r)/
disgusted (adj) /dɪsˈɡʌstɪd/
distance learning (n) /ˌdɪstəns ˈlɜː(r)nɪŋ/
district (n) /ˈdɪstrɪkt/
do a sponsored walk /ˌduː ə spɒnsəd ˈwɔːk/
do magic tricks /ˌduː mædʒɪk ˈtrɪks/
do research /ˌduː ˈriːsɜː(r)tʃ/
do the dishes /ˌduː ðə ˈdɪʃɪz/
do the housework /ˌduː ðə ˈhaʊswɜː(r)k/
do voluntary work /ˌduː ˈvɒlənt(ə)ri wɜː(r)k/
do work experience /ˌduː ˈwɜː(r)k ɪkspɪəriəns/
do your homework /ˌduː jə ˈhəʊmwɜː(r)k/
Don't just take our word for it! /ˌdəʊnt dʒʌst ˌteɪk aʊə ˈwɜː(r)d fər ɪt/
donate (v) /dəʊˈneɪt/
donation (n) /dəʊˈneɪʃ(ə)n/
(a) dream come true /ə ˌdriːm kʌm ˈtruː/
driverless car (n) /ˌdraɪvə(r)ləs ˈkɑː(r)/
drive-through restaurant (n) /ˌdraɪvθruː ˈrest(ə)rɒnt/
drive-thru (n) /ˈdraɪvˌθruː/

E

earn (v) /ɜː(r)n/
earthquake (n) /ˈɜː(r)θˌkweɪk/
easily (adv) /ˈiːzɪli/
edit a video /ˌedɪt ə ˈvɪdiəʊ/
edit photos /ˌedɪt ˈfəʊtəʊz/
editor (n) /ˈedɪtə(r)/
education (n) /ˌedjʊˈkeɪʃ(ə)n/
effective (adj) /ɪˈfektɪv/
effectively (adv) /ɪˈfektɪvli/
elevator (n) /ˈeləveɪtə(r)/
embarrassed (adj) /ɪmˈbærəst/
emergency services (n pl) /ɪˈmɜː(r)dʒ(ə)nsi ˌsɜː(r)vɪsɪz/
employee (n) /ɪmˈplɔɪiː, ˌemplɔɪˈiː/
employer (n) /ɪmˈplɔɪə(r)/
employment (n) /ɪmˈplɔɪmənt/
energy boost (n) /ˈenə(r)dʒi ˌbuːst/
enthusiastic (adj) /ɪnˌθjuːziˈæstɪk/
entrepreneurship (n) /ˌɒntrəprəˈnɜːrʃɪp/
equipment (n) /ɪˈkwɪpmənt/
e-reader (n) /ˈiːˌriːdər/
e-sports (n pl) /ˈiːˌspɔː(r)ts/
ethnicity (n) /eθˈnɪsəti/
evening classes (n) /ˈiːvnɪŋ ˌklɑːsəz/
exactly (adv) /ɪɡˈzæktli/
excited about (adj) /ɪkˈsaɪtɪd əˌbaʊt/
exciting (adj) /ɪkˈsaɪtɪŋ/
exhausting (adj) /ɪɡˈzɔːstɪŋ/
expensive (adj) /ɪkˈspensɪv/
exploitation (of sb to make money) (n) /ˌɪksplɔɪˈteɪʃ(ə)n/
extremely (adv) /ɪkˈstriːmli/
extremist (n) /ɪkˈstriːmɪst/
eye strain (n) /ˈaɪ ˌstreɪn/
eye-catching (adj) /ˈaɪˌkætʃɪŋ/
eye-witness report (n) /ˌaɪwɪtnəs rɪˈpɔː(r)t/

F

facilitate (v) /fəˈsɪləteɪt/
facilities (for sports/leisure) (n pl) /fəˈsɪlətiz/
faint (v) /feɪnt/
fair (n) /feə(r)/
fake (adj) /feɪk/

fake news (n) /ˌfeɪk ˈnjuːz/
fall out (with) (argue) (phr vb) /ˌfɔːl ˈaʊt/
fascinating (adj) /ˈfæsɪneɪtɪŋ/
fast (adv) /fɑːst/
ferry (n) /ˈferi/
film (n) /fɪlm/
find a balance /ˌfaɪnd ə ˈbæləns/
find a manufacturer /ˌfaɪnd ə ˌmænjʊˈfæktʃərə(r)/
finish off (phr vb) /ˌfɪnɪʃ ˈɒf/
firefighter (n) /ˈfaɪə(r)ˌfaɪtə(r)/
flat-pack machine (n) /ˌflætpæk məˈʃiːn/
flexible smartphone (n) /ˌfleksəb(ə)l ˈsmɑː(r)tfəʊn/
flood (n) /flʌd/
fly a kite /ˌflaɪ ə ˈkaɪt/
football (n) /ˈfʊtˌbɔːl/
fraudster (n) /ˈfrɔːdstə(r)/
freezing (adj) /ˈfriːzɪŋ/
friendships (n pl) /ˈfrendʃɪps/
frown (v) /fraʊn/
frustrating (adj) /frʌˈstreɪtɪŋ/
fundraise (v) /ˈfʌndˌreɪz/
funds (n pl) /fʌndz/
furious (adj) /ˈfjʊəriəs/

G

gamer (n) /ˈgeɪmə(r)/
gaming (n) /ˈgeɪmɪŋ/
gender (n) /ˈdʒendə(r)/
gesticulate (v) /dʒeˈstɪkjʊleɪt/
get a bank loan /ˌget ə ˈbæŋk ləʊn/
get a degree /ˌget ə dɪˈgriː/
get a holiday job /ˌget ə ˈhɒlɪdeɪ dʒɒb/
get a patent /ˌget ə ˈpeɪtənt/
get a reward /ˌget ə rɪˈwɔː(r)d/
get a suntan /ˌget ə ˈsʌntæn/
get distracted /ˌget dɪˈstræktɪd/
get on (with) (have a good relationship) (phr vb) /ˌget ˈɒn (wɪð)/
get online /ˌget ɒnˈlaɪn/
get organized /ˌget ˈɔː(r)gənaɪzd/
get sunburnt /ˌget ˈsʌnbɜː(r)nt/
get your hands on something /ˌget jə ˈhændz ɒn sʌmθɪŋ/

give (someone) a hug /ˌgɪv (sʌmwʌn) ə ˈhʌg/
give (someone) a hand /ˌgɪv (sʌmwʌn) ə ˈhænd/
give CPR (cardiopulmonary resuscitation) /ˌgɪv siːpiːˈɑː(r)/
give first aid /ˌgɪv fɜː(r)st ˈeɪd/
go abroad /ˌgəʊ əˈbrɔːd/
go backpacking /ˌgəʊ ˈbækpækɪŋ/
go for an interview /ˌgəʊ fər ən ˈɪntə(r)vjuː/
go on an exchange /ˌgəʊ ɒn ən ɪksˈtʃeɪndʒ/
go on strike /ˌgəʊ ɒn ˈstraɪk/
go out (with) (have a romantic relationship) (phr vb) /ˌgəʊ ˈaʊt (wɪð)/
go sightseeing /ˌgəʊ ˈsaɪtsiːɪŋ/
go snorkelling /ˌgəʊ ˈsnɔː(r)k(ə)lɪŋ/
go viral /ˌgəʊ ˈvaɪrəl/
gorgeous (adj) /ˈgɔː(r)dʒəs/
grant (sum of money given to a student) (n) /grɑːnt/
gym (n) /dʒɪm/

H

hack (a computer) (v) /hæk/
halfway through /ˌhɑːfweɪ ˈθruː/
handler (dog handler) (n) /ˈhændlə(r)/
hands-on (actually doing sth, rather than just learning about it) (adj) /ˌhændzˈɒn/
hang out (with) (spend time) (phr vb) /ˌhæŋ ˈaʊt wɪð/
happy (with) (adj) /ˈhæpi ˌwɪð/
harmful (adj) /ˈhɑː(r)mf(ə)l/
have a break /ˌhæv ə ˈbreɪk/
have a heart attack /ˌhæv ə ˈhɑː(r)t ətæk/
have a vlog channel /ˌhæv ə ˈvlɒg tʃæn(ə)l/
have stitches /ˌhæv ˈstɪtʃəz/
headline (n) /ˈhedˌlaɪn/
headset (n) /ˈhedˌset/
headset (for users of virtual reality technology) (n) /ˈhedˌset/

health and safety regulations (n pl) /ˌhelθ ən ˌseɪfti regjʊˈleɪʃ(ə)nz/
healthy eating (n) /ˌhelθi ˈiːtɪŋ/
heartbroken (adj) /ˈhɑː(r)tˌbrəʊkən/
help at an animal shelter /ˌhelp ət ən ˈænɪm(ə)l ʃeltə(r)/
high-speed train (n) /ˌhaɪspiːd ˈtreɪn/
hiking (n) /ˈhaɪkɪŋ/
hire a bike /ˌhaɪər ə ˈbaɪk/
hoax (internet hoax) (n) /həʊks/
hold a cake sale /ˌhəʊld ə ˈkeɪk seɪl/
hold hands /ˌhəʊld ˈhændz/
holiday (n) /ˈhɒlɪdeɪ/
hope (v) /həʊp/
horrific (adj) /həˈrɪfɪk/
hostility (n) /hɒsˈtɪləti/
hotel reception (n) /ˌhəʊtel rɪˈsepʃ(ə)n/
huge (adj) /hjuːdʒ/
hurt someone's feelings /ˌhɜː(r)t sʌmwʌnz ˈfiːlɪŋz/
hype (n) /haɪp/

I

identity theft (n) /aɪˈdentəti ˌθeft/
illogical (adj) /ɪˈlɒdʒɪk(ə)l/
illusion (n) /ɪˈluːʒ(ə)n/
illusionist (n) /ɪˈluːʒənɪst/
impatient (adj) /ɪmˈpeɪʃ(ə)nt/
importance (n) /ɪmˈpɔː(r)t(ə)ns/
improve the design /ɪmˌpruːv ðə dɪˈzaɪn/
inappropriate (adj) /ˌɪnəˈprəʊpriət/
incentive (n) /ɪnˈsentɪv/
ineffective (adj) /ˌɪnɪˈfektɪv/
inexpensive (adj) /ˌɪnɪkˈspensɪv/
inform (v) /ɪnˈfɔː(r)m/
infrastructure (n) /ˈɪnfrəˌstrʌktʃə(r)/
innovation (n) /ˌɪnəʊˈveɪʃ(ə)n/
innovative (adj) /ˈɪnəvətɪv, ˈɪnəveɪtɪv/
in person /ˌɪn ˈpɜː(r)s(ə)n/
inseparable (adj) /ɪnˈsep(ə)rəb(ə)l/
inspire (v) /ɪnˈspaɪr/
install updates /ɪnˌstɔːl ˈʌpdeɪts/

interactive (adj) /ˌɪntərˈæktɪv/
interested in (adj) /ˈɪntrəstɪd ˌɪn/
intern (n) /ˈɪntɜː(r)n/
internship (n) /ˈɪntɜː(r)nʃɪp/
interrupt (v) /ˌɪntəˈrʌpt/
invest (v) /ɪnˈvest/
invigilator (n) /ɪnˈvɪdʒɪleɪtə(r)/
invisible (adj) /ɪnˈvɪzəb(ə)l/
invite (v) /ɪnˈvaɪt/
involved in (adj) /ɪnˈvɒlvd ɪn/
irrational (adj) /ɪˈræʃ(ə)nəl/

J

jaw (n) /dʒɔː/
jealous (adj) /ˈdʒeləs/
jellyfish (n) /ˈdʒelifɪʃ/
jingle (advertising jingle) (n) /ˈdʒɪŋg(ə)l/
job prospects (n pl) /ˈdʒɒb ˌprɒspekts/
journalist (n) /ˈdʒɜː(r)nəlɪst/
juggle (v) /ˈdʒʌg(ə)l/
juggler (n) /ˈdʒʌglə(r)/
jump to conclusions /ˌdʒʌmp tə kənˈkluːʒ(ə)nz/
junk mail (n) /ˈdʒʌŋk ˌmeɪl/

K

keep an open mind /ˌkiːp ən əʊpən ˈmaɪnd/
kick-start (v) /ˈkɪkˌstɑː(r)t/
kid (Are you kidding?) (v) /kɪd (ˌɑː juː ˈkɪdɪŋ?/
kiss (sb) on the cheek /ˌkɪs (sʌmbədi) ɒn ðə ˈtʃiːk/

L

learn a foreign language /ˌlɜː(r)n ə fɒrɪn ˈlæŋgwɪdʒ/
learn first aid /ˌlɜː(r)n fɜː(r)st ˈeɪd/
leave a comment /ˌliːv ə ˈkɒment/
leave home /ˌliːv ˈhəʊm/
lecturer (n) /ˈlektʃərə(r)/
lend (v) /lend/
lend a hand /ˌlend ə ˈhænd/
levitate (v) /ˈlevɪteɪt/
lie on the beach /ˌlaɪ ɒn ðə ˈbiːtʃ/
lifeboat (n) /ˈlaɪfˌbəʊt/

lifeline (n) /ˈlaɪfˌlaɪn/
lift (n) /lɪft/
lift off (rocket) (phr vb) /ˌlɪft ˈɒf/
lighting (for a film/play) (n) /ˈlaɪtɪŋ/
lighting technician (n) /ˈlaɪtɪŋ tekˌnɪʃ(ə)n/
lightning (n) /ˈlaɪtnɪŋ/
likely (adj) /ˈlaɪkli/
link (on a website) (n) /lɪŋk/
live coverage (n) /ˌlaɪv ˈkʌv(ə)rɪdʒ/
live with (a serious medical condition) /ˈlɪv ˌwɪð/
lively (adj) /ˈlaɪvli/
loan (a bank loan) (n) /ləʊn/
location (n) /ləʊˈkeɪʃ(ə)n/
lock (v) /lɒk/
log on (phr vb) /ˌlɒg ˈɒn/
logical (adj) /ˈlɒdʒɪk(ə)l/
look after (phr vb) /ˌlʊk ˈɑːftə(r)/
look for an investor /ˌlʊk fər ən ɪnˈvest ə(r)/
luxury (n) /ˈlʌkʃəri/
lyrics (n pl) /ˈlɪrɪks/

M

magic (n) /ˈmædʒɪk/
magician (n) /məˈdʒɪʃ(ə)n/
make a choice /ˌmeɪk ə ˈtʃɔɪs/
make a decision /ˌmeɪk ə dɪˈsɪʒ(ə)n/
make a video blog /ˌmeɪk ə ˈvɪdiəʊ blɒg/
make arrangements /ˌmeɪk əˈreɪndʒmənts/
make eye contact /ˌmeɪk ˈaɪ kɒntækt/
make lists /ˌmeɪk ˈlɪsts/
make money /ˌmeɪk ˈmʌni/
make new friends /ˌmeɪk njuː ˈfrendz/
make up (with) (become friendly again after argument) (phr vb) /ˌmeɪk ˈʌp/
make-up artist (n) /ˈmeɪkʌp ˌɑː(r)tɪst/
marine biology (n) /məˌriːn baɪˈɒlədʒi/
market (v) /ˈmɑː(r)kɪt/
marketing stunt (n) /ˈmɑː(r)kɪtɪŋ ˌstʌnt/

meet a deadline /ˌmiːt ə ˈdedlaɪn/
meet up (with) (phr vb) /ˌmiːt ˈʌp (wɪð)/
membership (n) /ˈmembə(r)ʃɪp/
memory card (n) /ˈmem(ə)ri ˌkɑː(r)d/
memory chip (n) /ˈmem(ə)ri ˌtʃɪp/
mentor young people /ˌmentə jʌŋ ˈpiːp(ə)l/
message (v) /ˈmesɪdʒ/
minimum wage (n) /ˌmɪnɪməm ˈweɪdʒ/
money management (n) /ˈmʌni ˌmænɪdʒmənt/
mood (of an advertisement – silly/serious/sad, etc.) (n) /muːd/
moody (adj) /ˈmuːdi/
movie (n) /ˈmuːvi/
multi-task (v) /ˈmʌltiˌtɑːsk/
myth (n) /mɪθ/

N

nanotechnology (n) /ˈnænəʊtekˌnɒlədʒi/
nationality (n) /ˌnæʃəˈnæləti/
navigate (v) /ˈnævɪgeɪt/
navigation (n) /ˌnævɪˈgeɪʃ(ə)n/
negotiate (v) /nɪˈgəʊʃieɪt/
negotiation (n) /nɪˌgəʊʃiˈeɪʃ(ə)n/
nightmare (n) /ˈnaɪtˌmeə(r)/
noisy (adj) /ˈnɔɪzi/
non-profit organization (n) /ˌnɒnprɒfɪt ˌɔː(r)gənaɪˈzeɪʃ(ə)n/
non-verbal communication (n) /nɒnˌvɜː(r)b(ə)l kəˌmjuːnɪˈkeɪʃ(ə)n/

O

objective (an aim or purpose) (n) /əbˈdʒektɪv/
offer (v) /ˈɒfə(r)/
often (adv) /ˈɒf(ə)n/
on air /ˌɒn ˈeə(r)/
online ads (n pl) /ˌɒnlaɪn ˈædz/
operate (the lights for a film/play) (v) /ˈɒpəreɪt/
organize a talent show /ˌɔː(r)gənaɪz ə ˈtælənt ʃəʊ/
orphanage (n) /ˈɔː(r)f(ə)nɪdʒ/

out of your comfort zone /ˌaʊt əv jɔː ˈkʌmfə(r)t zəʊn/
outback (in Australia) (n) /ˈaʊtˌbæk/
outline (to describe in a general way) (v) /ˈaʊtlaɪn/
overwhelming (adj) /ˌəʊvə(r)ˈwelmɪŋ/
owe (v) /əʊ/

P

panicky (adj) /ˈpæniki/
paparazzi (n pl) /ˌpæpəˈrætsi/
(a) paper round (n) /ə ˈpeɪpə ˌraʊnd/
paramedics (n pl) /ˌpærəˈmedɪks/
part-time (adj) /ˈpɑːtˌtaɪm/
pass your driving test /ˌpɑːs jə(r) ˈdraɪvɪŋ test/
pass your exams /ˌpɑːs jə(r) ɪɡˈzæmz/
password (n) /ˈpɑːsˌwɜː(r)d/
patient (adj) /ˈpeɪʃ(ə)nt/
pay for (v) /ˈpeɪ ˌfɔː(r)/
peaceful (adj) /ˈpiːsf(ə)l/
peer group (n) /ˈpɪə(r) ˌɡruːp/
peer pressure (n) /ˈpɪə(r) ˌpreʃə(r)/
perform (v) /pə(r)ˈfɔː(r)m/
perform on stage /pə(r)ˌfɔː(r)m ɒn ˈsteɪdʒ/
performer (n) /pə(r)ˈfɔː(r)mə(r)/
personal space (n) /ˌpɜː(r)sən(ə)l ˈspeɪs/
personality (n) /ˌpɜː(r)səˈnæləti/
persuasive (adj) /pɜː(r)ˈsweɪsɪv/
phishing (n) /ˈfɪʃɪŋ/
phone-in (on a radio/TV programme) (n) /ˈfəʊnˌɪn/
photographer (n) /fəˈtɒɡrəfə(r)/
photo-manipulation (n) /ˌfəʊtəʊ məˌnɪpjʊˈleɪʃ(ə)n/
pick up (learn a new skill) (phr vb) /ˌpɪk ˈʌp/
PIN (Personal Identification Number) (n) /pɪn/
pitch (of sb's voice) (n) /pɪtʃ/
pitch (to try to sell sth by saying how good it is) (v) /pɪtʃ/
(work) placement (n) /(wɜː(r)k) ˈpleɪsmənt/
plan ahead (v) /ˌplæn əˈhed/

play in a band /ˌpleɪ ɪn ə ˈbænd/
playlist (n) /ˈpleɪˌlɪst/
pleased (adj) /pliːzd/
polluted (adj) /pəˈluːted/
pose as (pretend to be a particular person) (phr v) /ˈpəʊz ˌæz/
possessions (n pl) /pəˈzeʃ(ə)nz/
post (a comment on a website) (n) /pəʊst/
posture (n) /ˈpɒstʃə(r)/
precaution (n) /prɪˈkɔːʃ(ə)n/
presenter (n) /prɪˈzentə(r)/
press conference (n) /ˈpres ˌkɒnf(ə)rəns/
prestigious (adj) /preˈstɪdʒəs/
pretend (v) /prɪˈtend/
pretty (adj) /ˈprɪti/
prime time (period when most people watch TV) (n) /ˈpraɪm ˌtaɪm/
prioritize (v) /praɪˈɒrɪtaɪz/
problem-solving (n) /ˈprɒbləm ˌsɒlvɪŋ/
produce a prototype /prəˌdjuːs ə ˈprəʊtətaɪp/
promise (v) /ˈprɒmɪs/
promote (v) /prəˈməʊt/
promote a product (advertise it) /prəˌməʊt ə ˈprɒdʌkt/
promotion (n) /prəˈməʊʃ(ə)n/
props (furniture or other items used in a play/film) (n pl) /prɒps/
public space (anywhere where large numbers of people go, eg airport/train station) (n) /ˌpʌblɪk ˈspeɪs/
publish a blog post /ˌpʌblɪʃ ə ˈblɒɡ pəʊst/
put down (write sth on paper) (phr vb) /ˌpʊt ˈdaʊn/
put (someone) off (make someone not want to do sth) (phr vb) /ˌpʊt sʌmwʌn ˈɒf/
put (something) off (to delay doing sth) (phr vb) /ˌpʊt sʌmθɪŋ ˈɒf/

Q

qualification (n) /ˌkwɒlɪfɪˈkeɪʃ(ə)n/
quickly (adv) /ˈkwɪkli/
quite (adv) /kwaɪt/

R

raise (money) /reɪz (ˈmʌni)/
raise awareness /ˌreɪz əˈweə(r)nəs/
raise your eyebrows /ˌreɪz jər ˈaɪbraʊz/
rarely (adv) /ˈreə(r)li/
rational (adj) /ˈræʃ(ə)nəl/
receive a reward /rɪˌsiːv ə rɪˈwɔː(r)d/
receive compensation /rɪˌsiːv kɒmpenˈseɪʃ(ə)n/
record a video /rɪˌkɔː(r)d ə ˈvɪdiəʊ/
reference materials (dictionaries, etc.) (n pl) /ˈref(ə)rəns məˌtɪəriəlz/
refund (v) /rɪˈfʌnd/
refuse (v) /rɪˈfjuːz/
region (n) /ˈriːdʒən/
regret (v) /rɪˈɡret/
regulations (n pl) /ˌreɡjʊˈleɪʃ(ə)nz/
relationships (n) /rɪˈleɪʃ(ə)nʃɪps/
relieved (adj) /rɪˈliːvd/
remember (v) /rɪˈmembə(r)/
remind (v) /rɪˈmaɪnd/
remote control (n) /rɪˌməʊt kənˈtrəʊl/
replace (v) /rɪˈpleɪs/
reputation (n) /ˌrepjʊˈteɪʃ(ə)n/
requirement (n) /rɪˈkwaɪə(r)mənt/
rerun (of a TV series) (n) /ˈriːrʌn/
reschedule (v) /riːˈʃedjuːl/
rescue (n) /ˈreskjuː/
rescue cat (n) /ˈreskjuː ˌkæt/
residential (a residential course) (adj) /ˌrezɪˈdenʃ(ə)l/
resilience (ability to deal with problems) (n) /rɪˈzɪliəns/
respect for others /rɪˌspekt fər ˈʌðə(r)z/
retrieve (v) /rɪˈtriːv/
revise (for an exam) (v) /rɪˈvaɪz/
revision (n) /rɪˈvɪʒ(ə)n/
revision app (n) /rɪˈvɪʒ(ə)n ˌæp/
revision timetable (n) /rɪˌvɪʒ(ə)n ˈtaɪmteɪb(ə)l/
ride a unicycle /ˌraɪd ə ˈjuːnɪsaɪk(ə)l/
ringtone (n) /ˈrɪŋˌtəʊn/
risk (n) /rɪsk/
rock formation (n) /ˈrɒk fɔː(r)ˌmeɪʃ(ə)n/

roll your eyes /ˌrəʊl jər 'aɪz/
romantic (adj) /rəʊ'mæntɪk/
rumours (n pl) /'ruːmə(r)z/
(be) run by (the organization is run by volunteers) /ˌbi 'rʌn baɪ/
rush (v) /rʌʃ/

S

safe (adj) /seɪf/
safely (adv) /'seɪfli/
sample papers (exam papers set in previous years) (n) /'sɑːmp(ə)l ˌpeɪpə(r)z/
satellite broadband (n) /ˌsætəlaɪt 'brɔːdbænd/
save (money) (v) /seɪv/
savvy (adj) /'sævi/
say (v) /seɪ/
scam (n) /skæm/
scared (adj) /skeə(r)d/
scenery (in a play/film) (n) /'siːnəri/
screen-grab (n) /'skriːnˌgræb/
script (n) /skrɪpt/
scuba-diving (n) /'skuːbə ˌdaɪvɪŋ/
search and rescue workers (n) /ˌsɜː(r)tʃ ən 'reskjuː ˌwɜː(r)kə(r)z/
sector (n) /'sektə(r)/
see (v) /siː/
self-aware (adj) /ˌself ə'weə(r)/
self-awareness (n) /ˌself ə'weə(r)nəs/
send international aid /ˌsend ˌɪntə(r)ˌnæʃ(ə)nəl 'eɪd/
sensitive (sensitive documents) (adj) /'sensətɪv/
set (scenery used in a play/film) (n) /set/
set a reminder /ˌset ə rɪ'maɪndə(r)/
set designer (n) /'set dɪˌzaɪnə(r)/
set goals /ˌset 'gəʊlz/
set off (on a journey) (phr vb) /ˌset 'ɒf/
set your alarm /ˌset jər ə'lɑː(r)m/
settle down (begin to live a quieter life) (phr vb) /ˌset(ə)l 'daʊn/
shade (n) /ʃeɪd/
shake hands /ˌʃeɪk 'hændz/
shape (v) /ʃeɪp/

shark (n) /ʃɑː(r)k/
shred documents /ˌʃred 'dɒkjʊmənts/
shrug your shoulders /ˌʃrʌg jə(r) 'ʃəʊldə(r)z/
simulated mission (n) /ˌsɪmjʊleɪtɪd 'mɪʃ(ə)n/
sing (v) /sɪŋ/
singer (n) /'sɪŋə(r)/
slogan (advertising slogan) (n) /'sləʊgən/
slums (n pl) /slʌmz/
smart (adj) /smɑː(r)t/
smile (v) /smaɪl/
snack on (don't snack on sweets) (v) /'snæk ˌɒn/
soccer (n) /'sɒkə(r)/
social networking site (n) /ˌsəʊʃ(ə)l ˌnetwɜː(r)kɪŋ 'saɪt/
solve technical problems /ˌsɒlv 'teknɪk(ə)l ˌprɒbləmz/
sound effects (n pl) /'saʊnd ɪˌfekts/
soundtrack (n) /'saʊndˌtræk/
space station (n) /'speɪs ˌsteɪʃ(ə)n/
space tourism (n) /'speɪs ˌtʊərɪz(ə)m/
span (the Rocky Mountains span 5,000 km) (v) /spæn/
speak in public /ˌspiːk ɪn 'pʌblɪk/
spend (money) (v) /spend/
spending spree (n) /'spendɪŋ ˌspriː/
split up (with) (no longer be in a relationship) (phr vb) /ˌsplɪt 'ʌp/
staff (n) /stɑːf/
stand (a table at an exhibition where products are sold) (n) /stænd/
stare (v) /steə(r)/
start again /ˌstɑː(r)t ə'gen/
start off (phr vb) /ˌstɑː(r)t 'ɒf/
start over (AmE) /ˌstɑː(r)t 'əʊvə(r)/
starving (adj) /'stɑː(r)vɪŋ/
store (v) /stɔː(r)/
storyboard (series of pictures used for planning a film) (n) /'stɔːriˌbɔː(r)d/
strangers (n pl) /'streɪndʒə(r)z/
streaming (n) /'striːmɪŋ/
streaming site (n) /'striːmɪŋ ˌsaɪt/
stressed (adj) /strest/

strike (lighting strikes) (v) /straɪk/
study abroad /ˌstʌdi ə'brɔːd/
study space (a room or other area where you can study quietly) (n) /'stʌdi ˌspeɪs/
style (n) /staɪl/
subscribe (to a channel/blog) /səbˌskraɪb/
subscriber (n) /ˌsʌb'skraɪbə(r)/
subsidized (adj) /'sʌbsɪdaɪzd/
subtitles (n pl) /'sʌbˌtaɪt(ə)lz/
subway (n) /'sʌbˌweɪ/
suggest (v) /sə'dʒest/
sum up (give a summary of sth) (phr vb) /ˌsʌm 'ʌp/
sunset (n) /'sʌnˌset/
supporter (n) /sə'pɔː(r)tə(r)/
survival (n) /sə(r)'vaɪv(ə)l/
survival tip (n) /sə(r)'vaɪv(ə)l ˌtɪp/
survivors (n pl) /sə(r)'vaɪvə(r)z/
swim in the sea /ˌswɪm ɪn ðə 'siː/
swipe (move finger or cursor across an image rapidly in order to change it) (v) /swaɪp/
switch off (to relax and rest) (phr vb) /ˌswɪtʃ 'ɒf/

T

tablet (portable computer) (n) /'tæblət/
tabloid (n) /'tæblɔɪd/
tag (identify someone by name on social media) (v) /tæg/
take a break /ˌteɪk ə 'breɪk/
take a guided tour /ˌteɪk ə ˌgaɪdəd 'tʊə(r)/
take a photo /ˌteɪk ə 'fəʊtəʊ/
take cover /ˌteɪk 'kʌvə(r)/
take off (aeroplane) (phr vb) /ˌteɪk 'ɒf/
take part in /ˌteɪk ˌpɑː(r)t ɪn/
take someone's pulse /ˌteɪk ˌsʌmwʌnz 'pʌls/
take something into account /ˌteɪk ˌsʌmθɪŋ ˌɪntuː ə'kaʊnt/
talent contest (n) /'tælənt ˌkɒntest/
target (to try to influence a particular group of people) (v) /'tɑː(r)gɪt/

target audience (n) /ˌtɑː(r)gɪt ˈɔːdiəns/
taxi (n) /ˈtæksi/
teamwork (n) /ˈtiːmˌwɜː(r)k/
tell (v) /tel/
tell off (phr vb) /ˌtel ˈɒf/
terrifying (adj) /ˈterəfaɪɪŋ/
test a prototype /ˌtest ə ˈprəʊtətaɪp/
the best … in the world /ðə ˌbest ɪn ðə ˈwɜː(r)ld/
think creatively /ˌθɪŋk kriˈeɪtɪvli/
3D printing (n) /ˌθriːdiː ˈprɪntɪŋ/
throw away /ˌθrəʊ əˈweɪ/
time management (n) /ˈtaɪm ˌmænɪdʒmənt/
tiny (adj) /ˈtaɪni/
to cut a long story short /tə ˌkʌt ə ˌlɒŋ stɔːri ˈʃɔː(r)t/
tolerance (n) /ˈtɒlərəns/
tone (n) /təʊn/
torrential (rain) (adj) /təˈrenʃ(ə)l/
tourist brochure (n) /ˈtʊərɪst ˌbrəʊʃə(r)/
trace (v) /treɪs/
track (advertisers track our activity online) (v) /træk/
transcribe a video /trænˌskraɪb ə ˈvɪdiəʊ/
transferable skills (n pl) /trænsˌfɜː(r)əb(ə)l ˈskɪlz/
treat (going to the cinema is a treat) (n) /triːt/
trip (n) /trɪp/
try your hand at /ˌtraɪ jə ˈhænd æt/

U

ugly (adj) /ˈʌgli/
(the) Underground (n) /(ðiː) ˈʌndə(r)ˌgraʊnd/
underwater camera (n) /ˌʌndə(r)wɔːtə(r) ˈkæm(ə)rə/
unforgettable (adj) /ˌʌnfə(r)ˈgetəb(ə)l/
unlikely (adj) /ʌnˈlaɪkli/
unpack (v) /ʌnˈpæk/
unsubscribe (from an email subscription) (v) /ˌʌnsəbˈskraɪb/
update your blog/vlog /ʌpˌdeɪt jə(r) ˈblɒg/ˈvlɒg/
upload a photo /ʌpˌləʊd ə ˈfəʊtəʊ/
upset (adj) /ʌpˈset/
up-to-date (adj) /ˌʌptəˈdeɪt/
usually (adv) /ˈjuːʒʊəli/

V

vacation (n) /vəˈkeɪʃ(ə)n/
values (things you think are important) (n pl) /ˈvæljuːz/
vary (v) /ˈveəri/
very (adv) /ˈveri/
victims (n pl) /ˈvɪktɪmz/
video clip (n) /ˈvɪdiəʊ ˌklɪp/
viewer (n) /ˈvjuːə(r)/
viewing figures (n pl) /ˈvjuːɪŋ ˌfɪgə(r)z/
virtual (adj) /ˈvɜː(r)tʃʊəl/
visible (adj) /ˈvɪzəb(ə)l/
visit a museum /ˌvɪzɪt ə mjuːˈziːəm/
visual effects (n pl) /ˈvɪʒʊəl ɪˌfekts/
vocational (adj) /vəʊˈkeɪʃ(ə)nəl/
voice-activated (adj) /ˈvɔɪsæktɪˌveɪtɪd/
voluntary work (n) /ˈvɒlənt(ə)ri ˌwɜː(r)k/
volunteer (n) /ˌvɒlənˈtɪə(r)/
voyage (n) /ˈvɔɪɪdʒ/

W

wait (v) /weɪt/
wash up /ˌwɒʃ ˈʌp/
waste (money/time) (v) /weɪst/
watch (v) /wɒtʃ/
wear sun cream /ˌweə(r) ˈsʌn kriːm/
wearable gadgets (n pl) /ˌweərəb(ə)l ˈgædʒɪts/
well (adv) /wel/
well known for /wel ˈnəʊn fɔː(r)/
white-water kayaking (n) /ˌwaɪtwɔːtə(r) ˈkaɪækɪŋ/
wi-fi hotspot (n) /ˌwaɪfaɪ ˈhɒtspɒt/
win (a competition) (v) /wɪn/
win an award /ˌwɪn ən əˈwɔː(r)d/
withdraw (money) (v) /wɪðˈdrɔː/
work experience (n) /ˈwɜː(r)k ɪkˌspɪəriəns/
work in a charity shop /ˌwɜː(r)k ɪn ə ˈtʃærəti ʃɒp/
write a blog /ˌraɪt ə ˈblɒg/
write a business plan /ˌraɪt ə ˈbɪznəs plæn/
write a caption /ˌraɪt ə ˈkæpʃ(ə)n/
write a script /ˌraɪt ə ˈskrɪpt/
write a song /ˌraɪt ə ˈsɒŋ/
write computer code /ˌraɪt kəmˈpjuːtə(r) kəʊd/

Irregular verbs

Infinitive	Past simple	Past participle	Translation
be /biː/	was, were /wɒz/, /wɜː(r)/	been /biːn/	
beat /biːt/	beat /biːt/	beaten /ˈbiːt(ə)n/	
become /bɪˈkʌm/	became /bɪˈkeɪm/	become /bɪˈkʌm/	
begin /bɪˈgɪn/	began /bɪˈgæn/	begun /bɪˈgʌn/	
bend /bend/	bent /bent/	bent /bent/	
bet /bet/	bet /bet/	bet /bet/	
bite /baɪt/	bit /bɪt/	bitten /ˈbɪt(ə)n/	
bleed /bliːd/	bled /bled/	bled /bled/	
blow /bləʊ/	blew /bluː/	blown /bləʊn/	
break /breɪk/	broke /brəʊk/	broken /ˈbrəʊkən/	
bring /brɪŋ/	brought /brɔːt/	brought /brɔːt/	
build /bɪld/	built /bɪlt/	built /bɪlt/	
burn /bɜː(r)n/	burnt / burned /bɜː(r)nt/ /bɜː(r)nd/	burnt / burned /bɜː(r)nt/ /bɜː(r)nd/	
buy /baɪ/	bought /bɔːt/	bought /bɔːt/	
catch /kætʃ/	caught /kɔːt/	caught /kɔːt/	
choose /tʃuːz/	chose /tʃəʊz/	chosen /ˈtʃəʊz(ə)n/	
come /kʌm/	came /keɪm/	come /kʌm/	
cost /kɒst/	cost /kɒst/	cost /kɒst/	
cut /kʌt/	cut /kʌt/	cut /kʌt/	
dig /dɪg/	dug /dʌg/	dug /dʌg/	
do /duː/	did /dɪd/	done /dʌn/	
draw /drɔː/	drew /druː/	drawn /drɔːn/	
dream /driːm/	dreamt / dreamed /dremt/ /driːmd/	dreamt / dreamed /dremt/ /driːmd/	
drink /drɪŋk/	drank /dræŋk/	drunk /drʌŋk/	
drive /draɪv/	drove /drəʊv/	driven /ˈdrɪv(ə)n/	
eat /iːt/	ate /eɪt/	eaten /ˈiːt(ə)n/	
fall /fɔːl/	fell /fel/	fallen /ˈfɔːlən/	
feed /fiːd/	fed /fed/	fed /fed/	
feel /fiːl/	felt /felt/	felt /felt/	
fight /faɪt/	fought /fɔːt/	fought /fɔːt/	
find /faɪnd/	found /faʊnd/	found /faʊnd/	
fly /flaɪ/	flew /fluː/	flown /fləʊn/	
forget /fə(r)ˈget/	forgot /fə(r)ˈgɒt/	forgotten /fə(r)ˈgɒt(ə)n/	
forgive /fə(r)ˈgɪv/	forgave /fə(r)ˈgeɪv/	forgiven /fə(r)ˈgɪv(ə)n/	
freeze /friːz/	froze /frəʊz/	frozen /ˈfrəʊz(ə)n/	

Infinitive	Past simple	Past participle	Translation
get /get/	got /gɒt/	got /gɒt/	
give /gɪv/	gave /geɪv/	given /ˈgɪv(ə)n/	
go /gəʊ/	went /went/	gone /gɒn/	
grow /grəʊ/	grew /gruː/	grown /grəʊn/	
hang /hæŋ/	hung /hʌŋ/	hung /hʌŋ/	
have /hæv/	had /hæd/	had /hæd/	
hear /hɪə(r)/	heard /hɜː(r)d/	heard /hɜː(r)d/	
hide /haɪd/	hid /hɪd/	hidden /ˈhɪd(ə)n/	
hit /hɪt/	hit /hɪt/	hit /hɪt/	
hold /həʊld/	held /held/	held /held/	
hurt /hɜː(r)t/	hurt /hɜː(r)t/	hurt /hɜː(r)t/	
keep /kiːp/	kept /kept/	kept /kept/	
know /nəʊ/	knew /njuː/	known /nəʊn/	
lay /leɪ/	laid /leɪd/	laid /leɪd/	
lead /liːd/	led /led/	led /led/	
learn /lɜː(r)n/	learnt / learned /lɜː(r)nt/ /ˈlɜː(r)nd/	learnt / learned /lɜː(r)nt/ /ˈlɜː(r)nd/	
leave /liːv/	left /left/	left /left/	
lend /lend/	lent /lent/	lent /lent/	
let /let/	let /let/	let /let/	
light /laɪt/	lit /lɪt/	lit /lɪt/	
lose /luːz/	lost /lɒst/	lost /lɒst/	
make /meɪk/	made /meɪd/	made /meɪd/	
mean /miːn/	meant /ment/	meant /ment/	
meet /miːt/	met /met/	met /met/	
pay /peɪ/	paid /peɪd/	paid /peɪd/	
put /pʊt/	put /pʊt/	put /pʊt/	
read /riːd/	read /red/	read /red/	
ride /raɪd/	rode /rəʊd/	ridden /ˈrɪd(ə)n/	
ring /rɪŋ/	rang /ræŋ/	rung /rʌŋ/	
rise /raɪz/	rose /rəʊz/	risen /ˈrɪz(ə)n/	
run /rʌn/	ran /ræn/	run /rʌn/	
say /seɪ/	said /sed/	said /sed/	
see /siː/	saw /sɔː/	seen /siːn/	
sell /sel/	sold /səʊld/	sold /səʊld/	
send /send/	sent /sent/	sent /sent/	
set /set/	set /set/	set /set/	
shake /ʃeɪk/	shook /ʃʊk/	shaken /ˈʃeɪkən/	

Infinitive	Past simple	Past participle	Translation
shine /ʃaɪn/	shone /ʃɒn/	shone /ʃɒn/	
shut /ʃʌt/	shut /ʃʌt/	shut /ʃʌt/	
shoot /ʃuːt/	shot /ʃɒt/	shot /ʃɒt/	
show /ʃəʊ/	showed /ʃəʊd/	shown /ʃəʊn/	
sing /sɪŋ/	sang /sæŋ/	sung /sʌŋ/	
sink /sɪŋk/	sank /sæŋk/	sunk /sʌŋk/	
sit /sɪt/	sat /sæt/	sat /sæt/	
sleep /sliːp/	slept /slept/	slept /slept/	
smell /smel/	smelt / smelled /smelt/ /smeld/	smelt / smelled /smelt/ /smeld/	
speak /spiːk/	spoke /spəʊk/	spoken /ˈspəʊkən/	
spell /spel/	spelt /spelled/ /spelt/ /speld/	spelt /spelled/ /spelt/ /speld/	
spend /spend/	spent /spent/	spent /spent/	
stand /stænd/	stood /stʊd/	stood /stʊd/	
steal /stiːl/	stole /stəʊl/	stolen /stəʊl(ə)n/	
stick /stɪk/	stuck /stʌk/	stuck /stʌk/	
swim /swɪm/	swam /swæm/	swum /swʌm/	
take /teɪk/	took /tʊk/	taken /ˈteɪkən/	
teach /tiːtʃ/	taught /tɔːt/	taught /tɔːt/	
tear /teə(r)/	tore /tɔː/	torn /tɔːn/	
tell /tel/	told /təʊld/	told /təʊld/	
think /θɪŋk/	thought /θɔːt/	thought /θɔːt/	
throw /θrəʊ/	threw /θruː/	thrown /θrəʊn/	
understand /ˌʌndə(r)ˈstænd/	understood /ˌʌndərˈstʊd/	understood /ˌʌndərˈstʊd/	
wake /weɪk/	woke /wəʊk/	woken /ˈwəʊkən/	
wear /weə(r)/	wore /wɔː(r)/	worn /wɔː(r)n/	
win /wɪn/	won /wʌn/	won /wʌn/	
write /raɪt/	wrote /rəʊt/	written /ˈrɪt(ə)n/	